'Eclectic, brilliant and beautifully written, David George Haskell reboots our aromatic memory, reminding us of how our lives are intertwined with the wonder of trees.

A treat not to be sneezed at.'

SIR PETER CRANE, FRS

'Thirteen Ways to Smell a Tree is a transportive olfactory journey through the forest that sets the sense tingling. Every chapter summons a new aroma: leaf litter and woodsmoke, pine resin and tannin, quinine and bay leaf – life in all its glorious complexity. David George Haskell is a knowledgeable, witty and erudite companion, who takes us by the hand and leads us through the world, reminding us to breathe it all in.

This book is a breath of fresh air.'

CAL FLYN, AUTHOR OF
ISLANDS OF ABANDONMENT

THIRTEEN
WAYS
TO SMELL
A TREE

THIRTEEN WAYS TO SMELL A TREE

*Getting to know trees through
the language of scent*

David George Haskell

First published in Great Britain in 2021 by Gaia,
an imprint of
Octopus Publishing Group Ltd
Carmelite House
50 Victoria Embankment
London EC4Y 0DZ
www.octopusbooks.co.uk

An Hachette UK Company

www.hachette.co.uk

ISBN 978-1-85675-488-0

A CIP catalogue record for this book is available from
the British Library.

Printed and bound in the UK

10 9 8 7 6 5 4 3 2 1

This FSC® label means that materials used for the product
have been responsibly sourced

MIX
Paper from
responsible sources
FSC® C104740

Publisher Stephanie Jackson
Senior Editor Alex Stetter
Art Director Juliette Norsworthy
Typesetter Ed Pickford
Picture Research Manager Giulia Hetherington
Cover Illustration Katie Holten, Dair/Oak, Irish Tree Alphabet, 2020
Senior Production Manager Katherine Hockley
Chapter opener images **iStock** 16 Renphoto; 26 OlgaMiltsova; 34
vladm; 44 SoumenNath; 54 Staras; 64, 74 Renphoto; 82 SoumenNath;
92 da-kuk; 104 Antagain; 116 joey333; 130, 162 Sorapop; 144 sergio34;
PurePNG 10, 174

Contents

To teachers everywhere, both human
and more-than-human.

PREFACE

Tree aromas? What a curious topic. Yet, although we seldom think of them, trees and their smells pervade our everyday lives. Every aroma is an invitation to stories of interconnection between trees and people. The comforting, invigorating smell of a cup of tea reveals the character and origin of *Camellia sinensis* leaves. The delicious aromas of coffee and chocolate come from roasted, fermented tree seeds. The sharp, rich tang of nuts and olive oils brings trees to our dining tables. During the winter solstice holidays, cloves, figs, pomegranates, fir boughs and Christmas trees carry the scent of orchards and forests into our homes. Stepping outside, we inhale the aromas of trees, whether on city streets or in woodlands. And when it rains, we are bathed in tree smells – raindrops are seeded from clouds by aromatic molecules that trees send to the skies.

Slowing down to smell trees offers delight for our senses and a spur to curiosity. Why does the tree smell this way? What might I learn by following that aroma back to its ecological and cultural roots? Often, what we learn is a story of our bonds with others. No living being is alone. We live always in relationship with other species. Aromas are a reminder of the diversity of these life-giving connections.

Aroma is the most ignored and suppressed of the senses, yet it offers the swiftest and deepest links between the outside world and our memories and emotions, and enlivens all the other senses. Twitch your nose in readiness for a journey into a sensual relationship with our cousins, the trees. This is a multi-sensory experience, and so ready your ears, too. Violinist and composer Katherine Lehman has produced short musical pieces, each a reaction and accompaniment to the text, marvellous evocations of the diverse sensory presences and energies of trees and our relationships with them. You can hear them at soundcloud.com/katherinelehman/albums and in the audiobook edition.

David George Haskell

I.

HORSE-CHESTNUT, THE 'CONKER TREE'

Leeds, West Yorkshire, and
Denver, Colorado

VINTAGE: *circa* 1930

I stoop and pluck a spiky green ball from the lawn. Pressing my thumb into one of the three seams that divide its surface, I prise open the outer husk. Inside sits a gleaming mahogany seed with a dull, creamy cap. I'm in a city park in Denver, but as my thumbs bruise the protective shell and the seed emerges, a waft of aroma yanks me back in time to childhood trees in England. No Proustian madeleines for me. Instead, give me conkers.

Many senses powered this time travel. The prickle of the fruit in the hand. The shine of the conker. And, most of all, the strange union of odours as I release the horse-chestnut seed into my hand: from the green shell rises a salad bowl for the nose, wet and vegetative, tinged with composty tang where seams and spike tips have browned. The conker seed's aroma is tannic, like over-steeped tea. I smell a hint of something acrid and oily too, like bike-chain oil. Don't even think of eating me, these astringent aromas say. When I finally shuck the conker and sniff the empty shell, I smell a waft of apple core and fruity chewing gum, moist and sweet, then the odours dissipate and resolve into faint leafiness.

Adjectives and similes claw at fleeting impressions of dozens, perhaps hundreds, of aromatic molecules. The experience, though, needs no words. I am a child, playing with my sister and cousins, delighted to be back under the giant horse-chestnut tree down the road from my aunt and uncle's house, stuffing my pockets with treasure.

We have our neural wiring to thank for the speed and vigour of aromatic journeys. When the nose signals to the brain, it bypasses many of the filters and processing centres that refine and interpret our perceptions of light and sound. Smell plunges directly into remembrance and emotion, its messages carried by nerves that shoot into the brain regions for affective memory. *Sniff*...and we teleport directly to other times and places. Aroma of reheated mince pie: Christmas lights strung over the TV in my paternal grandparents' house in Portsmouth. Tang of a box of slug killer: that shelf in the garage of my maternal grandparents in Harrogate, just out of grasp of the reaching hands of children. Yeasty, woodsy smell of the bar at a pub: gathering of friends in London back in college days, conviviality after exams. Unshelled conkers: treasures weighing down my pockets, sister and cousins rushing about under the tree in Leeds on a sunny autumn day.

At the park in Denver, I remember, too, that pleasure delayed is pleasure lost. After just a couple of days, the shine and sharp smell of conkers dull. Over months, they dry and pucker, and lose their pleasing hand-heft. After a year, the handful of fat conkers that I piled into the coal-caboose of my toy train turn to meagre, shrivelled palmfuls like dried beans.

Even the pleasures of sparring with conkers are short-lived. We drilled the glossy seeds, trying not to pierce our hands as we impaled them on skewers or drilled with awls pilfered from our parents' toolbox. A few we soaked in vinegar, believing the schoolground tale that an acidic baptism would toughen the nuts for battle. We strung them on shoelaces, then swung our conker warriors at one another. The bulging ones cracked first. It was the scrawny, tight ones that prevailed: hard to hit and tight enough to deliver shattering blows. But none lasted more than a few rounds, confounding our hopes that careful preparations would yield a lasting champion. Dangling, broken on the end of the string, the conkers' white flesh smelled soapy and bitter. Anticipation and hope were more thrilling than the destructive work of combat.

Aromas pluck these joys and disappointments of childhood from the murk of my psyche, raising thoughts and feelings that had not entered my consciousness for forty years.

Aroma carries me inward, into memory, but also into direct physical contact with other creatures. Unasked for, parts of a tree – molecules that were made in plant cells and now drift in air – enter me and bind to my cell membranes. Some of these interlopers dissolve into my blood when I huff them into my lungs. The tree is on and in my body, bits of it quite literally clinging to me and swimming inside. Sight and hearing have the decency to use intermediaries – photons and sound waves – to connect us to others. Not so aroma, the most impudent of the senses.

The connection is ecological and historical, too. I'm sniffing conkers in Denver, but the tree evolved on another continent, in Eurasia. For over four hundred years horticulturalists have been importing to America exotic species they consider more beautiful or useful than indigenous ones, a form of botanical colonialism. Colorado has no shortage of magnificent trees, but this park is graced partly by the wide-spreading crowns of sylvan foreigners. In Leeds, too, I gathered the leavings of an immigrant. The horse-chestnut arrived in the British Isles in the 1600s, brought from the Balkan Peninsula by horticulturalists. The tree's five- or seven-fingered leaves, profuse garlands of springtime flowers, shady dome and copious conkers made it a favourite for plantings in parks and gardens, especially in the Victorian era. The same was true over much of Europe. In Germany, the trees are often used for shade in parks and other outdoor gathering spaces like beer gardens. Horse-chestnut is now so ubiquitous in British and

Northern European parks and gardens that we forget that this is a species whose character evolved in a different place. The bitter smell and taste of the seed are intended to deter the voles, squirrels, deer and boars of southern parts of Europe.

Part of the conkers' distinctive aroma, then, is a memory of the tussle between trees and their mammalian predators. The defensive chemicals that give the conker its nose bite may also deter weevils and other insects. Now, humans use these weapons of ecological struggle as medicine. Carefully measured doses of conker extracts can stimulate blood flow and relieve oedema. From the Thessaly Mountains to the urban parkland of Britain, and thence to our blood as aroma and medicine.

I leave most of the conkers in the grassy park for the children of Denver to discover. I lift one gleaming sylvan eye to my nose, though, and then slip it into my pocket.

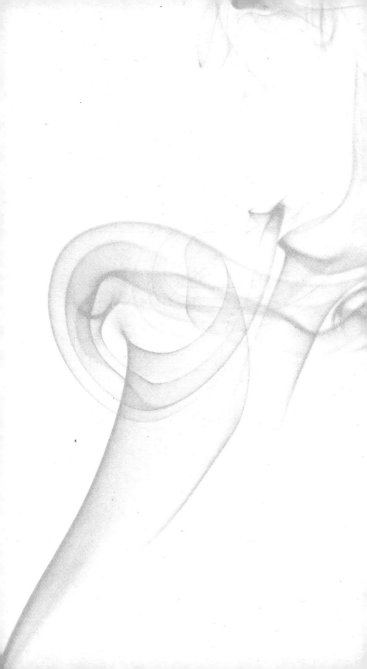

II.

AMERICAN BASSWOOD

Harlem, New York City

VINTAGE: 1908

Wе crack open the windows on summer's first warm days. The city's air flows into the stuffy interior, and I taste diesel smoke, acid and oily. The fumes rise from the bus stop directly under the fourth-floor apartment. The odour sinks to my gut, a bilious sheen. Across the street, an ice-cream truck runs its chugging generator all day, into the night. The truck parks there most afternoons and evenings, plying children with treats kept cool by the exertions of its decrepit engine. The exhalations cling high in my nose, a bitter sinus-cloud of exhaust.

These are aromas familiar to most modern humans. Pollution plumes flow to our lungs wherever coal, oil, charcoal, wood, diesel and petrol burn. Exhaust pipes and chimneys do not get rid of the toxic exhalations of our engines, they merely spread them out into millions of lungs. The particles lodge inside us. A few cross into the blood, poison our organs, accumulate in our brains. Globally, airborne fine particulate matter from the burning of fossil fuels causes over ten million premature deaths a year. Opening the window of our Harlem apartment unites us with the sensory experience of hundreds of millions of others. Tightness in our chests. Tarry odour in our noses and acid at the back of the throat. Like the smell of conkers, this aroma evokes memories, especially of London in the 1970s and 1980s when air pollution, although lower than the pea-soup smogs of the 1950s, was up to five times worse than it is today. To be outside, close to a road, was to be immersed in the odour and taste of exhaust. Our health remembers, too. Decades later, people in the United Kingdom exposed to bad air pollution in the 1970s have measurably poorer health than those who breathed clearer air. The experience of London air lives on within our cells.

In Harlem, on one morning in June, honey and wild rose reach through the window. A hint of lemon rind rolls close behind. Tree aromas smother and overwhelm the noxious combustion fumes.

For a full week, the street air is drunk on basswood flowers. The knots inside us loosen.

The American basswood trees that give us this aromatic delight are giants. They grow rooted in a roadside park across four lanes of gunning engines from our window. The basswood's flowers hang in clusters in the canopy. A few droop low, letting us see their creamy, star-like forms. Tens of thousands of these flowers exhale their chemical spells. Alongside them, lime trees originally from Britain and Western Europe, barely taller than saplings, seep their slightly sweeter aromas into the mix. The two species are close cousins and their aromas unite and wrap the neighbourhood in bliss.

The delight we feel on breathing these gifts is not just the result of relief from the monotony and unpleasantness of typical city odours. These tree molecules enter our cells and blood, calming us from within. Herbalists have long used tinctures and teas made from the flowers or leaves of basswood and its sibling, linden or lime, to soothe our harried nervous system. Biochemical studies concur. The tree's molecules are anodynes, soothing the nerves that tell us of pain. Just as diesel fumes flow into our blood and cells from the lungs, so, too, do the aromas of these trees. As the floral scent enters and embraces us, the trees lay a calming green hand on anxiety's brow, tranquilize the neural pathways of pain, and weave their aromas into the fractures in our central nervous systems. We breathe the tree, no longer dis-eased.

The fact that we can smell and respond to basswood flower aromas reflects our kinship with the insects. The basswood intends its aromas for bees and other insects, not us, an intention built into its genes and physiology by past natural selection. Despite being separated from the insects by more than six hundred million years, our nerves have the same cellular design, one inherited from yet more ancient ancestral animals. This similarity allows us to detect and enjoy signals sent from basswood to their pollinating bees: we detect aromas with many of the same cellular mechanisms. The same is true for the aromas of many other trees: plums, apples, quince and magnolias. A few trees, the pawpaw, for example, beckon to carrion-loving flies. Here, too, we can detect the aroma, but our evolution-ary background as picky eaters tells us to stay away from putrefaction.

The basswood flowers in Harlem fall to the ground later in June and the city reasserts its grip on our senses, a tight haze. But the tree's presence is not easily dislodged. Pleasure, especially unexpected sensual pleasure, is a powerful forger of memory. Now, thinking of the basswood years later, I still feel the tree's calming, rosy touch inside me.

III.

GREEN ASH

Boulder, Colorado

VINTAGE: 1980

On the narrow strip of grass between a pavement and a suburban house, I kneel at the pile of fresh wood chips. I scoop a double handful to my nose. A wet-green aroma: chopped lettuce and asparagus, backed by a whisper of tannin. Four hours ago, an ash tree stood here. Now, its trunk and limbs are gone, hauled off by the arborist's crew. A stump grinder's spinning maw turned the trunk's base and the upper roots into a heap of pulverized sawdust. A circle of golden leaves on the ground marks the extent of the canopy, an imprint that will be raked away by evening.

I lower my head and inhale again. I smell fennel and a hint of mushroomy soil. The odour is intense, as if I am diving in, mouth open. All at once, years of slowly accumulated aromas in the ash wood have been liberated into the air.

Further down this street, three other ash trees came down today. And, lately, across North America, hundreds of millions of ash trees have been felled, an erasure caused by one species of beetle, the emerald ash borer. Adult beetles are sparkly emerald lozenges, about half the length of a human thumbnail. When the sun hits them, their green carapace and wing covers shimmer with copper and gold. Bejewelled destroyers. After mating on the tree trunk, females stick fleck-like eggs into bark crevices. After hatching, the maggoty larvae burrow inward, through the tough bark to the sweet, nutritious living tree cells below. The larvae stay in this layer just below the bark, excavating tunnels as they move forward, munching on the tree's tissues. Combined, these tunnels can girdle a tree, cutting off the flow of sugars and other foods that usually pass under the bark. Choked from within, infected trees die within a year or two. Peel the bark from a dead trunk and the borers' tunnels look like the paths of hundreds of drunken ice-skaters, wiggling score marks all over the exposed wood.

North America hosts many indigenous wood- and bark-eating beetles. But disease and the attentions of woodpeckers and other birds mostly keep these hordes in check. The emerald ash borer is, however, a recent arrival and experiences few of the ecological restraints that control the populations of native beetles. With few local enemies, the emerald ash borer breeds and spreads with abandon. After colonizing a small part of southeastern Michigan, perhaps after a trans-Pacific journey on a packing crate, the beetle, in a little over a decade, expunged from city and forest alike one of North America's most common trees. Ashes are now rare or absent over much of their former range. In a few places, regular dousing with pesticides keeps the beetles away from special trees. Mostly, though, the ash trees are gone.

The near annihilation of these American ashes is a chilling foreshadowing of what might also happen to ashes in the United Kingdom. The emerald ash borer has spread to Russia and is moving west. British trees may meet the same fate as their American counterparts. A fungus adds to the peril. Arrived from Asia to the British Isles in 2012, the tree-killing fungus is poised to infect the one hundred and fifty million ash trees that live in British forests, parks, gardens and cities, including four million along roadsides. Projections of economic losses run to fifteen billion pounds sterling, but the ecological loss is immeasurable for a tree that, like American ashes, is a life-giving hub for other species. It seems that the novel fungus evades the trees' physiological defences that have evolved to keep indigenous fungi at bay.

The morning after the ash trees were cut, I return to the tree stump on our street. The odour of the pulverized wood is already muted. I smell churned soil and only a hint of yesterday's green.

The gentle aromas of ash leaves, complements to the sharpness of oak and the spice of pine, no longer thread through this neighbourhood. Houses stand unshaded along the edge of the road. The lush canopies of summer green and autumn gold are gone. The loss of ash trees has hurt the forest products trade, too. One particularly culturally significant loss in North America is of wood for baseball bats. Ash is a strong and lightweight wood and was formerly the preferred material for bat manufacture. The crack of an ash-wood bat onto a baseball was a sound heard all across the United States. But now, the sound has changed. Clanging aluminium bats dominate and other woods yield a mushy, wet sound as the ball strikes. A small difference, perhaps, but one symptomatic of the disappearance of an entire segment of commerce in wood products, especially furniture, cabinets, flooring and millwork. Human crafts, industries and livelihoods must now be built from narrower ecological foundation, an ongoing process as one native tree after another is lost or decimated by disease or insects from overseas. In America, the losses so far include chestnut, elm, hemlock and ash. In the UK, sixty million elm trees were lost to fungal infection, disease now threatens ash and oak, and boring insects are assaulting ash, birch and spruce.

These sensory losses for humans reveal a more significant ecological loss. Trees are smelters of life, now diminished. The native moth caterpillars that fed in the ash's leaves must find other hosts, as must the leaf miners, aphids and other insects that found sustenance from the tree. Likely most of these insects will not – the loss of a common tree species is not easily or quickly remedied by plantings or regeneration of other trees – and so the tree's disappearance unspools and diminishes some of life's network here. With no caterpillar and other insect morsels to pluck from leaves, migrating birds will struggle just a little more to fuel their passage from the tropics to the boreal forest.

The rush of aroma that I experienced as the ash was taken down was part of the language of trees. Human noses eavesdrop on the chemical messages that leaves, trunks and roots send to other members of the community. Plant cells both release molecules to the air and water, and their surfaces bristle with receptors for messages from others. Human terms for various aromas – 'leafy', 'sharp', 'bitter' or 'piney' – are poor translations of the complex and ever-changing blends of molecules that the plants send from one to another and to other creatures like microbes in the soil or insects winging past. Each molecule is like a word. A dozen molecules wafting from a leaf are botanical sentences, plant meanings writ in the grammar of organic chemistry. The changing nature of these blends – from morning to afternoon, from spring to autumn – are narrative arcs full of communicative meaning. Even with our most sophisticated laboratory equipment, we can parse only small portions of this language: a signal from root to microbe, initiating a cooperative union; a spritz of alarm from a wounded leaf, warning neighbours; and a call for help from leaf to predatory insects, a partnership united against herbivores.

To smell a tree is to join this conversation, albeit one spoken in a strange language with many hidden subtleties. For all its complexity, though, this tongue is not entirely inaccessible. As creatures whose ancestors lived for millions of years in forests and grasslands, our noses are tuned to some of the meanings of plant aroma. Amid the smell of healthy trees, we feel at home. Leafy odours of vigorous trees signal productive habitats and human well-being. The absence of such balm sets us on edge.

When a tree is hauled away and the denuded street smells only of wet asphalt and engine oil leaked from the arborists' old trucks, our bodies understand the loss of biological connection, vitality and possibility. Through ecological aesthetics – the appreciation and consideration of the perceptions of the senses – we are drawn into the stories of the other species around us, stories of both interconnection and impoverishment.

IV.

GIN AND TONIC

Worldwide

VINTAGE: 1870s

In your hand: a highball glass, beaded with cool moisture. Lift it to the light: ice cubes and clear sparkle, save for a haze, perhaps, where you dropped in a slice of lime.

In your nose: the aromatic embodiment of globalized trade. Inhale: the most vigorous note is the spiky, herbal odour of common juniper berries, the energizing smell of one of the northern hemisphere's most widely distributed trees, first added to gin by British, French and Dutch distillers. Alongside, a tang of lime juice, a hint of sweet citrus but mostly the bright, bitter smell of oils from the twisted lime skin. This fruit is from a tree descended from wild progenitors in the foothills of the Himalayas. Last, as you raise the glass to your lips, bitter quinine, from the bark of the South American cinchona tree, spritzed into your nostrils by the pop of sparkling tonic water.

Your drink was mixed by the hand of colonialism. The British in India dosed themselves with quinine to ward off malarial fevers. But quinine drunk alone is a bitter draught. And so, the gin and tonic was born by dissolving medicine in carbonated water and stirring in some gin. A dash of sugar and a wedge of lime added flavour and aroma, especially when the lime's skin was slightly twisted to release its store of oils. An imperial troika of trees: juniper, cinchona and lime.

Juniper arrived in the drink through its flavouring and preservative properties. For centuries, the astringent oils of juniper berries flavoured and preserved the meats, beers and spirits of Northern Europe. In Britain, the berries are especially favoured for game meats and mulled wine. Gin, distilled from grain but flavoured with juniper, is named for the tree – *genevre*, the Old French word for juniper. By the eighteenth century in Britain, gin was cheaper and flowed more abundantly than beer. In 1750, Britons drank eleven million gallons of gin and in some parts of London, one in five houses was a gin shop. Gin inevitably followed British trade and war routes. Juniper's aroma found its way to other continents as colonists carried their tastes across the seas.

In the tropics, gin soon found a sylvan companion. An infusion made from alkaloids in the bark of South American cinchona trees eases malarial fevers by killing off many of the malarial parasites in the patients' blood. The medicinal qualities of the bark were well known to indigenous peoples of the region and colonial Jesuits learned of its powers in the seventeenth century. Spanish colonists in South America then developed and monopolized trade in the bark. *Cascarilleros*, 'bark workers', laboured in teams in the forest. After locating a cinchona tree, they stripped away the vines that covered it, removed the tough outer bark that had no value to them, then felled the tree. Once the trees were on the ground, the *cascarilleros* cut and peeled the medicinal inner bark which, after drying, was packed into large bales for shipping. For two centuries, the Spanish controlled trade in the bark, sending it to Europe, where malaria was endemic, and to other colonies. When added in low doses to carbonated water, quinine made a slightly bitter drink, enlivened by the fizz of bubbles. In 1858, Erasmus Bond patented his 'improved aerated tonic' as a digestive aid and nerve toner, marketed and sold in Britain. In the 1860s, advertising expanded to the British colonies where it was touted as a digestive and fever remedy.

After the Spanish started to export the bark in the seventeenth century, demand surged as colonial expansion continued. Wild cinchona populations in South America were decimated. Spurred by scarcity and the great value of the bark, British, French and Dutch botanists eventually found cinchona seeds and smuggled them to Europe. From there, European horticulturalists then established plantations in Asian colonies, especially in Java in the nineteenth century. Chemists isolated the active compound – quinine – and mastered the extraction process. Plantations and factories fed an industrialized supply chain. By the early twentieth century, ninety per cent of the global trade in quinine from cinchona came from Dutch colonial farms in Asia. In 1880, nearly three million kilograms of bark were shipped from Java to Europe. Oscillations in price, though, ruined many cinchona farmers, leading in 1913 to a 'Quinine Agreement' among producers, processors and buyers which set a minimum price for the bark. This was the world's first pharmaceutical cartel. Quinine remained the main treatment for malaria until new, synthetic anti-malaria drugs were invented in the 1940s.

Lime's journey to the glass of gin and tonic, too, was powered by its medicinal effects, with a boost from the delight humans take in its acidic tang. As a source of ascorbic acid – vitamin C – lemons and limes were favoured by the British navy as a ward against scurvy. The fruits kept well in ships' holds and a daily dose kept the sailors healthy. Limes have less of the precious vitamin than lemons and are therefore much less effective, but in the early nineteenth century the navy was ignorant of this fact and therefore shipped limes worldwide in its fleet, mostly sourced from Caribbean plantations. Limes also arrived in lime-infused tonic waters shipped for the retail trade. In sending limes from the West Indies to colonies in India and other parts of Asia, the British were creating an unintended homecoming for the plants. The citrus clan of plants first diversified about seven million years ago in southern Asia. People then domesticated the plants in different regions using extensive cross-breeding of different wild species to create the fruits we know today. The 'lime' in my gin and tonic and in most supermarkets is a hybrid between lemon (a sour orange/citron hybrid, native to northern parts of India) and Key lime (another hybrid, native to tropical Southeast Asia).

Take a sip, feel the aromas and tastes of Asia, South America and Europe converge.

Gin and tonic manifest for our nose and palate the global tangle of trees in our lives. We sit on furniture assembled from unknown forests across the world, read paper sourced from plantations thousands of miles away, live in buildings made from dozens of trees reconfigured into plywood and lumber, and dine on fruits and oils brought to us by modern colonial trade networks.

The highball glass, beaded with cold sweat, is a mirror.

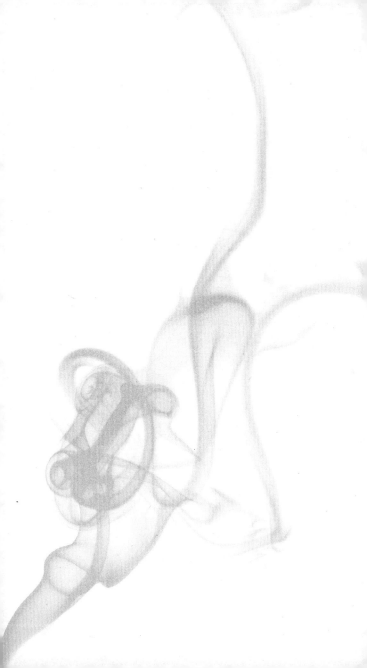

V.

GINKGO

Sewanee, Tennessee

VINTAGE: *circa* 1930

Ugh! *Gak*! Disgust erupts as college students pass under the tree's spreading branches. Their feet dance jigs, twitching up and skipping sideways. A few take leaping strides in their haste to escape. A profusion of stinking apricot-like blobs circles the ground under the tree. Their presence has animated the usual nonchalance of walkers between dormitory and dining hall.

The tree, a giant ginkgo planted in the early twentieth century, holds up a middle finger to college quadrangle aesthetics, as it does on campuses and city parks all over the northern hemisphere. I love it for its defiance. Here is messy fecundity on full display, an affront to the mown, suppressed conformity of the tidy campus lawns. The ginkgo scoffs at such prissiness. The lawn grass is forced into the illusion of perpetual sexless youth, an effect achieved with synthetic herbicides, nitrogen-rich fertilizers from factories and spinning blades powered by fossil fuels. These are joined by the regular passage of leaf-blowers, devices that take modern ecological absurdity to its highest level: burning the remains of dead photosynthetic creatures (petrol) to achieve minor rearrangements of the positions of yet more dead photosynthetic creatures (fallen leaves). The grasses are thus allowed no display of profligate reproduction. Nor are the other trees on the quadrangle. They are chosen for their demure characters, species whose flowers and fruit leave few reminders on lawns and paths of aromatic, fleshy sex.

Hundreds of mushy silvery-orange globules litter the ground under the ginkgo tree. I inhale the odours: rancid butter. Oily beards of billy goats turned rank by their braggart streams of piss. Vomit. These emanations combine to make a wall of icky smell, the aromas of over-ripeness and decay. The odour comes mostly from butyric and hexanoic acids, the same molecules released when butter and cheese's oils decay, when fats in animal oils fester and when we puke the hidden fermentations of our guts. No wonder the students exclaimed and pranced as they walked to breakfast.

The ginkgo's aromas delight me not only for their discomforting effect on the present, but because they tie my senses directly to life's deep history. Ginkgo has lived nearly unchanged for about two hundred million years, one of the most august lineages among all plants. Leaf impressions from rocks nearly three hundred million years old seem to belong to close relatives or perhaps even ancestors of ginkgo. By two hundred million years ago, fossil leaves show ginkgo's distinctive fan-like shape, almost indistinguishable from modern species. By sixty-five million years ago, fossil remains seem identical to modern plants. We call the species a 'living fossil', but there is nothing fossil-like about the tree. Indeed, it has a fuller sensory presence here than most, both in its aroma and the stunning gold colour of its autumn leaves.

The first ginkgo-like plants evolved in the Permian, before the giant supercontinent Pangaea broke apart. Ginkgo in its near-modern form graced forests worldwide in the Jurassic and Cretaceous, leaving abundant fossil evidence of their wide range and ecological prominence. From the end of the Cretaceous, sixty-five million years ago, to the present, wild populations oscillated, but over the long term declined then disappeared, first from the southern hemisphere then gradually across the northern continents. By about a million years ago, ginkgo was extinct worldwide, except in an enclave in southwestern China.

The aromas of ginkgo are a reminder of its relationships with long-extinct animals. We don't know exactly which species dispersed the ginkgo's seeds in ages past, but dinosaurs with a taste for putrefaction, along with ancient mammals and birds, likely swallowed the smelly, pulpy surrounds of the seeds, distributing the ginkgo's progeny in their dung. Today, ginkgo fruits attract scavenging leopard cats, palm civets and raccoon dogs in the temperate forests of Asia. But the vast majority of ginkgoes are now propagated by people, either from cuttings or seeds planted in nurseries. In China, ginkgoes have been in cultivation for at least a thousand years. Elsewhere, their popularity is mostly a twentieth-century phenomenon.

Despite the unpleasant smell of the flesh, the meat inside the seed is nutritious and used both in cuisine and, when dried, as a medicine. On some mornings, I see an elderly couple harvesting at this tree, arriving before students are out of bed. They wear thick rubber gloves as they toss the ginkgo seeds into plastic buckets. They tell me they roast them for snacking. Likely the food value of the seed that the couple so enjoy, along with the beauty of the leaves, first brought the tree into cultivation.

We humans have taken over the seed-dispersing work of the dinosaurs, but the aroma is bereft: its function as an attractor for animals has largely disappeared in this new world. Instead, humans shun odoriferous female trees, culling young trees in the nursery or grafting male branches onto rootstock. My senior colleagues tell me that the female tree that now festoons our campus with smelly balls was, for decades, the only ginkgo for dozens of miles and, as a consequence, received no ginkgo pollen and produced no seeds wrapped in smelly flesh. Then, male ginkgoes were planted on adjacent quadrangles and tree sex commenced, an unintended outcome of horticultural additions to campus.

As I walk under the tree, I think, too, of the melted stone and metal of Hiroshima. The first and often the only life to grow back after the nuclear blast were ginkgo trees at the temples in the city. Deep roots and physiological resilience carried the trees through a calamity that killed all else. Ginkgo's ability to withstand assault also accounts for the tree's presence on polluted city streets. The tree weathers the chemical and physical challenges of urban life and is a favourite of urban horticulturalists. Ginkgo leaves have relatively few breathing pores, compared to many other trees, an advantage where air is not always healthy. In polluted areas, the interiors of ginkgo leaves grow thicker, protecting the cells inside. The tree may also be able to modify the fats in its cell membranes to withstand excess road salt.

Ginkgo is now mostly a species of the street, its roots sunk into openings in pavements in London, Tokyo, New York and Beijing. No other street tree can rival the ginkgo for the vitality of its summer green or the arresting intensity of its autumnal gold. In London and Manhattan, I've often seen people stopped in their tracks by sunlight on the autumn leaves of ginkgo. Yet, complaints from city dwellers about the aroma of their squishy seed flesh also abound on streets where the trees are common.

As I feel the mucilage of ginkgo fruits underfoot and the odour of rot in my nose, my imagination is drawn into other places and times. Ginkgo trees' stink is more than an amusing foil for the tidiness and sexlessness of campus plantings. In my nose is the aroma of life's persistence, a pungent reminder that a tree's generative power can prevail amid the convulsions of mass extinctions, the break-up of continents, the noxious air and soil of crowded cities, and the annihilation of nuclear war.

I stop under the tree, inhale deeply, and embrace the putrid glory of life.

VI.

PONDEROSA PINE

Bear Canyon, Santa Fe,
New Mexico

VINTAGE: various, *circa* 1700 to 2000

W^e are cocooned in the sun-warmed aroma of a bakery. As we stroll up the canyon's gentle slope, pine duff softens our footfall. All around, the flaky amber bark of ponderosa trees seeps its vanilla and butter confection into the hot summer air. There is no breeze today, and humidity is low, as it usually is in this dry landscape, and so we swim through a mist of delight. Ponderosa is famed for its gorgeous scents, yet this canyon's welcome seems to surpass all others: glowing, rich and mellow. Unlike most other conifers that hold tight to their scent, revealing them only to close-pressed noses, this species perfumes the entire canyon.

Ponderosa is a delight not only for the succulence and abundance of its bouquet, but for how its aroma reveals the individuality of each tree. Every trunk has a distinctive personality. We learn, through our noses, a general truth about trees. Like us, they have their individual dispositions and histories. Mostly, these variations are hard for human senses to grasp. But ponderosa pine, unlike many trees, does not tuck away and hide its inner life behind aroma-trapping bark. Instead, its aromas are strong and pleasant enough to entrance even the most inattentive visitor in their groves. This gives us an excuse to stop, wrap an arm around the trees and press our noses to their bark. What, tree, is your name? What is your character?

The blend of dozens of volatile chemicals gives each tree its aromatic signature. Among these are the monoterpenes, molecules whose structures are variations on the same molecular theme, ten carbon atoms stitched together in rings and strings. Small rearrangements of these patterns yield molecules with different aromas. Pinene has the harsh, astringent smell of turpentine. Limonene is the zest of lemon rind. Myrcene is bruised thyme, pleasant and calm. Carene evokes fir needles and sweet resin, more mellow than pinene. These and dozens more variants of carbon origami form part of the aerial language of plants. Alongside these are various alcohols and aldehydes, including the familiar warm smell of vanillin. With so many constituent parts, every breath of odour from leaf and trunk can encode thousands of different meanings and identities.

An old tree, its trunk twice the girth of most in the canyon, is unlike all the other ponderosas here. It produces no vanilla aroma at all. Instead, the tree smells resinous, like cedar, with a tang of bitter turpentine. The elder's trunk bleeds resin from hundreds of insect-inflicted holes. This is a tree with no scent of ease, just the sharp bite of chemicals deployed by a creature fighting for its life. Lab experiments confirm that stressed or wounded ponderosas tilt their resin away from gentle limonene and toward harsh pinene. This may help deter insects, but also signals the news of distress to neighbouring plants.

Other ponderosa trees in the canyon have a more uniform ambrosial aroma, but nonetheless with close, attentive inhales, each tree is recognizably different from the others. On the drier, hotter slopes the trees have overtones of alcohol, tannin and leather. These hints of darkness are scarce here, more typical of trees further north, in the Colorado Front Range where sniffing trees sometimes feels like lifting glasses of bourbon to your nose. The largest trees, their bark often split by scars of long-ago lightning strikes, have odours edged with burned brown sugar and caramel. Or are my eyes confounding my nose, making me smell the fire? Younger trees, especially those in the well-watered base of the canyon, release a guileless butterscotch, with no hint of trouble or edge. From my sniffing of trees through the year, I know that these are the aromas of the growing season. In winter, flows of resin slow and the cold restrains the liveliness of aromatic molecules. But even in the snow, every tree has its character. In January, some ponderosas are, to my nose, silent, but others sing their aromas to the chilly sun.

The odour of each individual reveals both its pedigree and the nature of its local environment. Parent trees with lemony resin – more common in ponderosa from the Pacific side of the Rockies – pass along their chemical proclivities to their offspring, for example. Just as animal voices – bird, whale and insect song, and human languages – have regional dialects, so too do the voices of trees. Presumably the trees of each region are adapted to the moisture and insects of their homes. Within each habitat, individual saplings experience unique combinations of soil, water, tree neighbours, browsing mammals and tunnelling insects. Tree personality, revealed by aroma, is a melding of heredity and experience.

What we humans experience as aromas, trees use to communicate and defend. Their airborne molecules connect trees, delivering precise messages about forest news. *Where are the hungry mandibles of the enemy? Reply to me in our dialect.* For some species, the right mix of chemicals is interpretable only to trees with kindred sap. In lodgepole pine trees, for example, trees with similar aroma profiles, most likely kin, responded to one another's aromatic signals about attacking fungi, but not to signals from other trees. Like humans that pay special attention to people speaking with the same accent as them, these trees seem to discriminate between chemical signals from kin and strangers. In this way, clans whisper to one another through the forest air. The ancient society of trees is conspiratorial as well as collaborative, a fruitful tension. Our dullard noses and understanding are as yet able to grasp only the edges of these conversations.

The same molecules sicken and kill insects, severing or befuddling the links between their nerve cells. If a tree senses insects chewing into its trunk or leaves, or receives an alert from a neighbour about such attacks, it boosts its production of the more insecticidal chemicals. The predators of tree-chewing insects – carnivorous and parasitic beetles and wasps – sniff the air for these defensive aromas of trees and use them to home in on their prey. The chemicals may signal to mammalian noses, too, albeit indirectly. Deer, porcupines and Abert's squirrels all prefer to browse on less aromatic trees.

Ponderosa's mortal enemies, mountain bark beetles, add a cunning twist to this chemical dialogue. When feeding, they pilfer tree monoterpenes and then tweak their chemical structures. The result is a powerful pheromone. The refashioned molecule, blended with other beetle aromas, summons a mob of other beetles. These invaders cluster on an individual tree and launch a mass attack. The bark beetles turn the tree's shield into a spear.

The earthbound drama mediated by pine tree aromas drifts upward and changes the sky. Yearly across the globe, vegetation sends a million million kilograms of aromatic molecules to the air. Isoprene is the most common one from tropical forests, a molecule with a slight aroma of petrol. For pine forests, pinene dominates. This great heavenward exhalation of trees primes the sky for rain. Each aromatic molecule remains in the air for only a few hours before it degrades or is reabsorbed by living beings, but during this time it can become the seed around which raindrops first gather. Some molecules clump together and form seeds directly. Others stick to motes of dust, making the tiny particles stickier and more attractive to water vapour. The sky is partly made of forest. Next time it rains, know that many of the falling raindrops were born on exhalations of trees.

The delight I feel in the ponderosa's aromas joins me to the communicative heart of the forest. Trees confide in one another. Insects eavesdrop and concoct. Earth and sky converse.

VII.

PINE TREE HANGING FROM THE REAR-VIEW MIRROR

VINTAGE: patented 1954

The cardboard tree hanging from the London cabbie's rear-view mirror swings violently as we take the corner. The slicing motion looses pine and lemon scent from between fibres of compressed cellulose. We get a gust of forest air, right here in the car's interior.

Drive for a few minutes in any city or on any highway and look closely, especially at the windscreens of taxis, delivery drivers and other professional road warriors. In some places, half of the vehicles have a cardboard tree hanging behind the windscreen, odourizing the interior. Today, these trees-on-strings come in many aromatic varieties, each one with its own colour and image printed on the cardboard, and so the aromatic character of each car or truck is revealed by a glance. In Britain and Europe, LittleTrees® 'Arctic Ice' is popular, promising a 'modern, refreshing fragrance with a hint of citrus', touted as a 'masculine' and 'outdoor' aroma. In the United States, the pastel clouds of 'Cotton Candy' will 'bring back childhood memories with this sweet blend of spun sugar, strawberry, and vanilla'. The 'America' tree, printed with the flag, delivers the 'signature Vanillaroma® scent'. America, apparently, is best represented by a trade-marked synthetic analogue of a natural product.

In some locations, local law forbids anything from obstructing the view through the windscreen, and so these dangling trees offer police ready-made excuses to pull people over. It is surprising, then, that one of the aromas is the 'rich scent of barrel-aged Kentucky bourbon', surely a choice that drivers might regret when rolling down the window to greet an officer of the law. On the other hand, a booze-scented air freshener might provide a cover for the same aromas on the breath. *I haven't been drinking, officer, it's my tree that smells of liquor.*

The delightful aromatic diversity of these modern trees is rooted in old-fashioned pine scents. When Julius Sämann first patented the hanger, cellophane wrapper and string – a combination that allows aroma to diffuse from a card within finger-protecting packaging – he intended it to carry the fresh aromas of pine forests. His first patents, in 1954, featured a large-busted woman arching her back, perhaps someone who had spent so much time in the forest that she smelled of evergreen trees. Five years later he took a step back from the objectification of women and patented a similar device in the shape of a pine tree. His inspiration for the invention was a complaint from a milk-truck driver about the aroma of spilled milk. In the 1950s, more people were spending time in cars and trucks, part of the suburbanization trend, yet there were few ways at that time to control the aroma of the vehicle. As a chemist with experience in extracting aromas from trees, Sämann saw an opportunity to bring aromatic molecules into cars.

The tree has stopped swinging. We are stuck in a traffic jam. Gasoline by-products and nitrogen oxides stream from tailpipes. When sunlight hits the fumes, the pollutants seethe and react, making ozone. Our car interior now becomes a chemistry experiment. Monoterpenes originally from trees blend with the nitrogen oxides and ozone from the traffic, all held inside an enclosed space. When chemists replicate the experiment in the lab, the reactions of 'air freshener' chemicals with pollutants yield a mist of invisible particles and organic gases. This happens outside, too. Wherever traffic fumes, especially nitrogen oxides, merge with the aromatic molecules of trees, ozone and then fine particulate matter are created. The aromatic molecules that trees and other vegetation release to the air not only give forest air its characteristic aroma and seed raindrops in the sky above, but become part of the mix of pollutants in urban areas.

Inside the car, the mix of tree aroma and traffic fumes potentially creates a hazard not only to the lungs but the other tissues of the body. So, too, do the other gases born in lab experiments that mix air fresheners with pollution: acetone, formaldehyde, acrolein and acetaldehyde. How these mixtures apply in the real-life context of a cardboard tree in a car interior, though, is hard to assess. The experiments that mixed and measured these chemicals were done in controlled spaces in the lab.

The modern era has turned the healthful breath of a forest into something more troubled and ambiguous. Trees scrub some pollutants from the air and, when planted in a city, can reduce pollution by absorbing particles from the air. Some trees even detoxify pollutants inside their leaves. Leafy neighbourhoods are usually less polluted than open streets. But on days when nitrogen pollution is high and trees are pouring their aromas to the sky, the air is hazed with particulate pollution from the collision of tree breath, sunlight and burned fossil fuel. In the future, it is likely that planting of trees along busy streets will be partly guided by the aromatic signature of each tree species, not to please human noses but to minimize pollution. Maples, for example, emit far less isoprene than plane trees. Lime trees produce almost none. And so, to minimize city pollution, plane trees might work best away from traffic, in parks, but lime and maple could line busy thoroughfares.

Traffic eases and we pull away. The aroma-tree on the rear-view mirror swings like an incense censer dangling from a priest's hands. It waves its odours over us as we drive, delivering the dubious benediction of modernity.

VIII

WAYGARGAH OR ANTARCTIC BEECH

Queensland, Australia

VINTAGE: unknown, likely many centuries

A giant limb has snapped from the trunk, exposing smooth laminations of wood in the torn stub. At its centre, the branch is maroon, as if soaked by red wine. Wrapped around this core are layers of cream-coloured wood, smooth to the touch where the violence of the fall has peeled them apart. I lift this striking two-toned scar to my nose. I'm stunned by the gentle aroma. Despite the damp wind chilling me, the tree conveys warmth and calm. Buttery pastry fresh from the oven. The aroma of the sun on ripe apples. But these impressions quickly fade. The limb came down just minutes ago and already the wood is surrendering its inner life to the breeze.

The English common name for this tree, Antarctic beech, reveals confusion and arrogance among colonial botanists. Seeing a superficial similarity between the tree's light wood and toothed leaves and the beech trees of Britain, they imported the name and classified the trees among beeches and oaks. The scientific name, *Nothofagus*, means 'false or illegitimate beech', a slur. But these trees have a different story to tell than being false southern versions of trees from a 'truer' imagined English motherland. They are instead descendants of the forests of the ancient southern supercontinent, Gondwanaland, and are members of their own plant family with a history that dates to the Cretaceous, ninety million years ago. Today, forty-three species of the *Nothofagus* genus live all across the southern hemisphere, from Chile to New Zealand. They were common in Antarctica before it froze, as evidenced by the fossilized leaves and wood that are found under the ice there now. In the Bundjalung-Yugambeh language of the traditional custodians of this land, the tree is called waygargah (perhaps related to *waygan*, for the 'upper side', a tree found at elevation), a name indigenous to the place and with no colonial biases or misunderstandings.

The distinctive aroma of the wood in the fallen branch, so unlike the sharper tang of beeches and oaks, is a product of waygargah's evolutionary path on Gondwanaland. Studies of leaf chemistry show that every species of the *Nothofagus* genus possesses its own distinctive combination of aromatic molecules. The Antarctic beech that dropped the giant limb seems to be the mildest, lacking some of the molecules found in close relatives. The ecological and evolutionary causes of these differences are unknown. We do know that the aromas deter plant-chewing insects, and so it is likely that each tree has adapted itself to the suite of herbivores that live in its habitat.

Here, at the easternmost edge of Australia, the habitat of waygargah is unique and harbours insect species found nowhere else, including descendants of some of the first insects to suck on plant saps. These creatures now live down in the lush moss on tree branches, a habitat that has likely not changed much in tens of millions of years. This special ecosystem owes its continued existence to the climate conditions created by an extinct volcano. This one-hundred-kilometre-wide eroded caldera is rimmed with high ridges. Winds blowing from lowland eucalyptus forests, cattle pastures and

Pacific shores cool as they swoop up the escarpment. This sudden chill causes water vapour held in the air to condense into billowing fog. Dense clouds stream through the forest, even when the rest of the landscape lies under blue skies. Waygargah and all the insects that depend on it cling to life in this wet, cloudy zone. The trees live within a sliver of possibility: winds with enough moisture, temperatures just right. The population persists on a strip of land hardly wider than a couple of trees' branch span. In their thriving, they bring to our senses the richness of Gondwanan rainforests.

I heft the limb to the side of the trail and return to the earthy aroma that enfolds the rest of this huge, gnarled tree. The fulsome odour of wet peat. A hint of tannic decay. The sharpness of fern fronds. Walking in the forest here is like swimming through a moss world. I'm a springtail, a tardigrade, a nematode, miniaturized by the huge trees, enveloped in moss. Every trunk and branch is swaddled. Fern stems snake through the verdant thickets on branches, poking their paddle-like leaves above the tangle. It's likely that the water-saturated weight of this lush wrap is partly what broke the limb at my feet. Every tree branch is a sky-lake and forceful gusts push wood beyond its limits.

On this isolated mountain ridge, the trees make their own rain. The mop of moss and the dense thatch of tree leaves intercept the river of fog as it comes across the lip of the caldera. Droplets from this fog land on the tree and accumulate. The tree and the vegetation growing on it pull water out of the clouds. Moss and ferns on the tree branches hold on to some of their water harvests, supping on the sky. The rest of the water falls, ringing the ground below each tree with moisture. Every tree is a rain-maker, standing at the centre of a circle of wet earth. The ground between these halos is dusty dry.

The constant moisture and relatively even temperatures of this habitat – heatwaves and freezes are rare here – create a hospitable place for the trees, many of which live for centuries. When old stems fall, new ones resprout from the living roots, creating a bulging, gnarled base. So old are many of the trees that the slow erosion of soil from around them has left each tree standing on root stilts a metre high. The massive scale of roots and trunks overwhelms me. The spaces between roots are large enough to contain my whole body.

This temperate rainforest's lush aroma is like that of the rocky seashore, without the salty bite. A fecund exultation at the meeting place of water, sky and life. The seashore's aroma is an ancient triumph, started by the first algae and land plants on Paleozoic shores, over four-hundred-and-fifty million years ago. Water-sucking roots and moisture-quickened leaves since then have carried the union of moisture and plant forward to the present day. Here, in the Gondwanan forests, the celebration reaches a zenith, water and terrestrial plant life flowing into one another, lifting tree giants from the ground, soaking the air in the odours of green.

IX.

WHITE OAK

Edinburgh, Scotland, and
Sewanee, Tennessee

VINTAGE: 1830

In front of me at the bar in Edinburgh are three small glasses of gold-amber liquid, a tasting flight. Two Scotch whiskies and one Kentucky bourbon. I swirl, sniff and sip the first scotch. Peaty smoke, tannic oak: dark and invigorating. The second scotch has a tannic undertone but is warmer and sleepier, with no smokiness. I smell hints of vanilla and dark toffee. Then the bourbon: caramel and spice to the nose, peppery and sweet on the tongue.

Each has its own character, revealing the different grains, malting processes and casks used to produce and mature the whisky. Malted barley roasted over peat fire retains the aromatic imprint of its smoky origins. Barley roasted without smoke has a brighter finish. The sweetness of corn, moderated by rye's more subtle and dark touch, gives bourbon its honey. But despite this diversity, what unites these whiskies is oak, usually American white oak. By law, bourbon is matured in new oak casks. After the bourbon is drawn off, many of these casks then travel by sea to Scotland to spend their dotage encasing scotch. Some scotches use sherry casks, including those made from European oaks. To smell and sip a whisky is to dive into the sensory world of oaks, a place of tannins, woody astringency and caramelized sugars.

The oaky signature of the whiskies is so clear that, as I stand at the bar, my nose draws me into memories of stacking wood at my former home in Tennessee. I remember white oak, in particular, for its gorgeous aroma.

Every summer, I'd load a truck with cut white oak and dump in onto the driveway, ready for splitting and stacking. Cleaving the cut log segments with a maul, then building them into tidy rows to cure, I felt the reassuring weight of fuelwood in my shoulders. Each piece of wood was an ingot of sunlight, a store of life-giving heat. The oak tree assembled these molecules in its leaves, then transported them down to the trunk, adding new layers of wood year by year. Except for some minerals from the roots, the wood is made entirely of air, water and sunshine.

My muscles understood the meaning of the weightiness of wood: a sense of security in having a winter's worth of heat neatly stacked up and stored, ready for the cold. My nose did, too. The splitting and slinging of oak raise a satisfying mist of woody aroma. Mostly sharp, sweet tannin, a dark tea spiced with cloves. Bitter and hot. This is oak's most distinctive aroma, found in fallen trees, firewood, boards and barrels. Wood from heartwood smells tart enough to sting nostrils. Over the years, oaks build up tannins and defensive chemicals in the wood at the core of the tree, slowing rot. Lighter woods from the trunk's edges have overtones of coconut and of singed sugar.

The white oak whose wood I remember stacking died earlier that same year. Its afterlife as a snag and then fallen log could have nourished fungi and many animals for decades. Over half of the animal species in these Tennessee forests depend on dead wood for one part of their life cycle, from food for millipedes, to nesting sites for snails, to winter protection for salamanders. But, for this tree that grew on a roadside, the danger of falling limbs condemned it to removal from its place on the verge. Given that its growth rings dated it to 1830, the tree was older than the road. It germinated when this part of Tennessee was still Cherokee territory, before genocidal forced removals put the land in the hands of Europeans. I salvaged the wood from the municipal burn pile, a pit on the edge of town dug into the sandstone. The town managers periodically torch the wood at the pit, sending years' worth of wood energy skyward. For this tree, a portion of what would have been waste burned through my stove.

White oak was a lucky find at the dump. Stacking the wood, I was bathed in the aroma of wine and whisky barrels. Now, at the bar with my flight of three whiskies, the aromas carry me back to the pleasant work of splitting logs and the roughness of oak wood on my hands as I stack the firewood. But had I found red oak, I'd have smelled vinegar and old engine oil, the result of high concentrations of volatile organic molecules in the wood. Tolerable, but not a delight. Had I found pin oak, I'd have left it at the dump. Split, it reeks of tomcat urine, a smell that fades only after a couple of years of seasoning. Piss oak is its local name. The heavy load of acrid chemicals in its wood presumably suits it to its native habitat, swampy, clay-heavy soils where the threat of rot is ever-present.

Like connoisseurs of fine whiskies, squirrels are also attuned to oak aromas and tastes in the forests of eastern North America. In autumn, multiple oak species drop their acorns at about the same time. The squirrels immediately gobble up acorns of white oak, but store those of red oak for later. White oak acorns have lower concentrations of bitter tannin than red oak acorns, just as their wood does. And so, the squirrels eat the sweeter white oak acorns first, saving the red oak acorns for later. This choice gives them another advantage. White oak acorns germinate soon after falling to the ground, sending out a small taproot and converting some of the stored starchy energy in the acorn into miniature leaves. White oak acorns therefore do not store well. But red oak acorns stay dormant all winter, germinating in the spring. By storing the bitter acorns, the squirrels succeed in caching food that stands the best chance of being nutritious late in winter.

My whisky- and oak-sniffing is amateur, an apprentice's coarse taxonomy. Vintners and whisky makers understand the nuances much better, often making distinctions not just between different oak species, but within regional variants of a single species. Traditionally, red wines, bourbon and whisky were all aged in oak barrels. No piss oaks or red oaks, just white oaks from eastern North America or Europe. The heartwood is best, having the highest concentrations of the right tannins and other flavourful molecules. Over weeks, months and sometimes years the barrel staves ease their woody songs into the liquor. Today, steel vats house parts of the fermentation process for some, but then, for all bourbons, most whiskies and some red wines, the maturing liquid is transferred to oak barrels. Now that oaks, especially European oaks, are scarcer than in centuries past, barrels are reused and shipped from one continent to another. A glass of scotch contains the melded aromas of two continents.

Not all white oak behaves the same way in the barrel. Tight-grained white oak from Minnesota slowly eases its aromas and flavours into the liquid inside and its tannins are subtle and rounded. Virginia's trees are more open-pored and eager to share their spice. European oaks evoke hazel and dark smoke. All this aromatic subtlety is adjusted by the barrel-making process where the cooper applies flame to the empty barrels' interiors before filling. The extent of the burn changes the aroma and flavour: a mere lick yields spiciness, a good toast brings vanilla and toffee, and a heavy burn roasted coffee. The barrel's terroir and treatment are as much a part of drinks' aromas and flavours as are peat smoke, grapes and grain.

We're not alone in savouring plant tannins and their aromatic chemical allies. The diet of most herbivores, especially those that browse on wood and leaves, is a feast of these molecules. Every plant species has its own aroma and taste, and every leaf on the plant has its own signature. It takes time for tannins to build up, and so the concentration of tannins often increases as leaves age. Watch a deer or goat use its lips and tongue: they sift through vegetation, plucking their favourites with great precision. Discerning palates and noses benefit the animals. At low doses, tannins and other tasty plant chemicals are antifungal, antibacterial and antioxidative. Animals with stomach upsets will seek out tannic food, self-medicating to purge intestinal parasites. We do the same, including in our diets tannin-rich foods and drinks like tea, coffee, wine and many fruits, and dosing ourselves with tannic herbs when ill. Tannins have a bitter and astringent mouthfeel, and some of them slow the release of other aromas to the nose. Compare lightly steeped and over-steeped cups of tea: aromas in the first are subtle and multi-layered. In the second, tannins dominate, especially when we take a sip and our mouths pucker.

Tannins are there to defend the plant. These bitter chemicals can be disruptive and even poisonous. In the acid of vertebrate guts, tannins bind proteins and can ruin digestion. In insects, many of which have alkaline digestive systems, tannins do not bind to proteins, but instead oxidize molecules and cells in the gut, essentially burning the insects from the inside.

Browsing mammals take countermeasures and often have saliva tuned to the tannic mélange of their favourite foods. Moose saliva subdues the tannins in aspen and birch, beaver saliva is adapted to willow, mouse to acorn, mule deer to their diverse diet of trees, howler monkeys to tropical leaves and black bear saliva works on all kinds of tannins, as befits an omnivore. Human salivary proteins, like the bears', are primed to meet a wide variety of plants. Our saliva is tannin-ready all year, not just seasonally as in many other species.

I stand at the bar and take a slow inhale from my whisky glass. A comforting aroma. Like stacked firewood or barrel-aged red wine, oak aromas are a signal of home and shelter. We are ready for winter, warmed by oak.

X.

BAY LAUREL

Paris, France

VINTAGE: 1980

Smell is the most ancient of senses. Before life evolved eyes and ears, cells conversed in the language of molecules. Cell membranes, then and now, bristle with protein receptors, each one an antenna waiting for chemical signals from other cells both near and far. When the right chemical binds to its surface, a receptor protein changes its shape, and either sets off a cascade of reactions inside the cell or causes a sudden shift in the electrical charge on the cell membrane. And so, the arrival of a chemical – an aromatic molecule – is alchemized into biological activity in the cell. From molecule wafting in air to action in the cell, then, in our case, sensation in a human body.

Ten to twenty million olfactory receptor cells crowd inside our human noses. Each one is a nerve cell that pokes its bristly head into the thin layer of moisture that lines the top of the nasal cavity. The bristles receive chemicals from the air, grab onto them, then shoot signals to the rest of the nerve. This signal then zips to the brain. We have about four hundred receptor types in our noses. Compare that to the five different light receptor types in our eyes (red, blue and green rods; low-light 'grey' cones; and a nerve type that picks up background glow). Theoretically, if we paid attention to what our noses are telling us, our odour perception could distinguish among a trillion different combinations of molecules, a hyper-rainbow of aroma.

These receptor cells in our noses are vulnerable. Unlike almost all other cells in the body that hide under protective skin, the heads of these cells are exposed to whatever we inhale. This brings them into direct contact with toxins and pathogens. The thin layer of mucus that covers them – a sheen that we dismiss as mere snot – is a sophisticated protective bath. Within this bath are antibodies and enzymes that find and neutralize harmful chemicals and invading cells. Despite this help, olfactory receptor cells have a hard and short life. Most live only a couple of months. Our sense of smell depends on their continual renewal. Openness and vulnerability lead not only to danger, but to intimacy. Our sense of smell connects us in a direct way with other beings. When we smell a tree, we become physically connected to a small part of it, molecule-to-molecule. The boundary between tree and human blurs, just a little.

Smell is not only an ancient cellular process, it is also the sense most immediately and strongly connected to human memory and emotion. When an aroma arrives at our nose, nerves signal to the olfactory bulb in the brain, then to the base and centre of the brain: the amygdala, which processes emotion, and the two hippocampi, which process memory. Other senses pass through layers of interpretation and mediation. Aroma is more direct. It arrives in our bodies first as deeply felt bodily remembrance and affect. Our brains later add a veneer of language and conscious perception, but this is literally an afterthought.

What tree aromas evoke memory and emotion for you?

Evergreen trees and festive holidays? In the scents of pine, fir and spruce, we remember the emotions of the solstice season. We mark our hope for renewed life in the darkest time of the year by bringing green boughs into our homes. There, they lodge in memory as their aromas suffuse us.

Cloves and allspice in a hot mug of apple cider? These aromas often evoke memories of warmth and comfort: stamping feet in the cold around a bonfire or gathering in a kitchen while the winter rains beat on the windows.

The floral, waxy smell of date confectionary? The aromas of celebrations and treats in the Middle East and North Africa. A union of tree, flower and sugar.

The piney-clean smell of a classroom after the floors have been scrubbed? I remember the antiseptic smell of a clattering school hallway, still wet from mopping, animated by the tromp of children's feet.

The dusty sting of cedar wood shavings from a sharpened pencil? This is a smell that anticipates either the dread of an exam or the joy of spending time drawing on a clean sheet of paper.

A haze of leafy aromas in a city park after summer rain? Even in the middle of a busy city, when the rain falls, the aromas of leaves and soil envelop us, stirring memories of summer rainstorms. The raindrops wet and stir the trees' surfaces, activating aromas and carrying them to the air. As rainwater seeps into soil crevices, it pushes out the air from the spaces among sand and clay particles, an exhalation from the dark world of the soil. Unlike so many other smells, this one is so distinctive that we give it a name, petrichor.

These memories, different for each one of us, reveal the nature of our childhoods and early lives. Tree aromas are portals, flying us back into our experience of the culture that raised us.

For me, the bay tree is one such portal. *Laurus nobilis* is a staple of Mediterranean stews and soups. Where I grew up, as a British ex-pat in France, it is most often used in casseroles for aroma and flavour, just as it is in cuisines all over Europe and the Middle East. Generally, after cooking, we discard the spent leaf before serving. Bay leaf's smell evokes for me the gentle simmer of a stew whose flavours will mingle for hours, in a pot large enough to feed several people. The aromas rise in the steam. They fill the kitchen and curl into neighbouring rooms, carrying the knowledge that food will be here soon, but not yet. Delayed gratification.

On the palate, bay reveals the interlinked natures of smell and taste. Before taking a bite, the aroma is a vigorous blend of eucalypt and cardamom, with hints of pepper, lavender and clove. These are the aromas that arrive through the nostrils, flowing directly to the receptors in our nasal cavities. In the mouth, though, the experience shifts. Flavours arrive at our taste buds, dissolved in saliva or the fluids of our food. Unlike the hundreds of receptor types that greet aromas in the nose, the tongue's sensory cells are focused on detecting combinations of sweetness, bitterness, saltiness, sourness and umami. These sensations then run to a different part of the brain, the gustatory cortex, than the nerves that come from the nose. But despite these differences, smell and taste are not independent. Their interpretations of food mingle in our conscious perception, producing a unified response to the experience of eating. This is helped by a second pathway for aromas to the nose. When we chew or swallow, aromatic molecules rise up into the nasal cavity from the back of the throat. This 'retro-nasal' route, through what amounts to a hidden third nostril, allows us to appreciate the aromas of our foods as we eat them, further blending the senses of smell and taste. For foods cooked with bay leaves, the taste of the bay is often slight, but the aroma strong. The experience of smelling a stew therefore gives us a more vigorous sense of the bay's presence than eating. In the mouth, other flavouring plants – thyme and rosemary, especially – dominate the conversation with vegetable and meat. But if we should be foolhardy enough to pluck a bay leaf from the stew and bite down, the bitterness receptors of our mouths erupt in protest. Of all the seasonings, bay leaf is the friendliest to the nose but the most hostile to the tongue.

Warm kitchen, good food and family. As with other aromatic memories, the bay leaf doesn't just suggest these associations to me. It *is* them. Its aroma plunges me directly into deep memory, activating my mind and emotions from within. If you mapped all the people who share this memory of the aromas of bay, you'd draw the rough contour of Mediterranean cooks and diaspora around the world. But this would be a crude map of the link between bay leaf and human memory. For many Italians, pasta sauces or risottos, not stews, would be bay's companion in memory. For anyone raised with Syrian Aleppo soap, bay is the aroma of warm water and scrubbing: bath time.

Bay leaves did not, of course, evolve to give us pleasure. Instead, the molecules that we perceive as aroma and taste have a defensive intent. Specialized cells in the leaf manufacture, store and secrete these chemicals, mostly in the form of oils. About two hundred different chemicals combine in the unctuous blend. When we cook the leaf, the heat breaks open cells, releasing the oils, suffusing our foods with a low concentration of the bay plant's defensive chemical arsenal. But when an insect bites into the leaf, it gets the full effect, a mouthful that poisons the attacker's nerves and digestive system. Likewise, when bacterial or fungal cells try to invade a bay leaf, the interlopers are bathed in toxic oils. The dose makes the poison: either lethal chemical weaponry or delightful flavouring. Or, between these two extremes, medicine. Bay leaf extracts help to regulate blood-sugar levels in diabetics, and are antimicrobial and antioxidant.

Bay trees have good reason to be well defended. They evolved in subtropical forests whose mild climate made insect life especially abundant. Unlike deciduous trees whose leaves last a mere few months before they are shed, bay laurel is evergreen and its leaves last more than a year. Every thick, leathery leaf is therefore a significant and precious investment for the tree, well worth defending with copious oils. The same is true for other plants such as olive and myrtle that lived alongside laurel in forests that once dominated much of Europe, the Middle East and North Africa. In the lush and aromatic foliage of these species we get a hint of an ancient world. Before the Ice Ages and our present relatively cool and dry era, laurel forests grew in a mild and wet climate for millions of years over a large swath of what is now arid Eurasia and Africa.

Bay leaf aromas are guides back into wordless memory – of good meals from my childhood, yes, but also into the history of vegetation in the Mediterranean. I inhale the satisfying aroma of a bay-infused stew, and awaken human and ecological memory.

XI.

WOODSMOKE

Forests worldwide

VINTAGE: today

The smoke from wood fires made us. It may also be our undoing.

One million years ago, and perhaps half a million years before that, small bands of walking apes, most likely *Homo erectus*, gathered at campfires inside caves in southern Africa. The evidence they left was scant – tiny fragments of burned bone and ashed leafy vegetation – but clearly shows that these early hominins used fire. Later, from about four hundred thousand years ago, both Neanderthals and modern humans made habitual use of fire.

For these ancestors and cousins of modern humans, the smell of smoke was the aroma of home and of progress. Burning wood was an evolutionary catalyst. Flames warmed, kept predators at bay, hardened spears, flaked stone tools, produced birch tar and cooked food, nourishing and protecting our ancestors. Fire killed pathogens in food and released nutrients, allowing our brains to expand and technologies to flourish.

Fire also catalysed culture. By drawing us into close circles, the campfire knitted together our minds and emotions, intensifying and deepening human social interactions. To this day, when we gather at the fire, our blood pressure drops and conversation turns to the realm of the imagination. We are calmed by the sight, sound and smell of a friendly bonfire or campfire, and soon bond with others around its warmth, sharing stories. Human society was born around wood flames.

No wonder, then, when we gather for ritual or celebration, we light a fire. Burning plant material is the centre of many religious rituals, solstice celebrations, rites of passage, and informal social gatherings. The aroma, sounds and hues of burning wood promise pleasure in meeting others and unity in the community. We're an unusual mammal, loving fire and going out of our way to bring it into our homes. Most others flee its dangers.

Even when the fire is fuelled by modern natural gas or compressed charcoal we hunger for the sensory experience of a real wood fire. We add burned wood aromas with bags of wood chips thrown onto gas grill fires. Smoky flavours for food come in jars of seasoning. Flame-mimicking light-bulbs and online streaming videos bring the dance of flames to our eyes. These artifices suggest that part of being human is to crave the sensory visual, aural and aromatic experience of fire.

But wood smoke also maims, kills and distorts. A waft of smoke after a day's work might initially smell of ease and conviviality. The same smoke inhaled over weeks and years wreaks havoc inside us.

At least four hundred different chemicals combine in wood smoke, most of them harmful: carbon monoxide, nitrogen oxides, benzene, and hundreds of other irritating, neurotoxic and carcinogenic molecules. Wood smoke also hazes the air with billions of microscopic flecks of partly burned wood. This particulate pollution damages lungs and triggers asthma attacks. Once in the lungs, the particles enter our blood, inflaming us, literally, from within, damaging our organs.

Human evolution seems to have reduced this physiological threat. Humans carry a gene that makes them less sensitive than other primates to the irritating and toxic effects of smoke. The form of this gene in humans dials back our reactivity to toxins that rise out of burning wood. The distress of our forebears gave us this resistance: those who suffered too much under smoky conditions passed on fewer genes, a measure of the past burdens imposed by wood fires. A few others, those endowed with the right mutations, thrived, or at least persisted, despite the soot and fumes. Yet, even with this ability – unique among primates – to live and reproduce in conditions that sicken and kill other species, we humans still feel the ill effects of smoke.

Those who cook over open fires are at most risk. The World Health Organization estimates that three billion people worldwide rely on open fires or stoves fuelled by wood, kerosene, dung, crop residues or coal. These smoky fires damage lungs, nervous systems, blood vessels and hearts, resulting in four million premature deaths. Half of child-hood deaths due to pneumonia are caused by sooty household air.

Even in countries where most people cook with electricity or natural gas, wood smoke is a hazard.

In the United Kingdom, annual emissions of particulate pollution from domestic wood burning more than doubled from 2003 to 2019 and now accounts for thirty-eight per cent of this kind of air pollution. In Sweden and New Zealand, seventy per cent of wintertime fine particle pollution is from wood burning. In upstate New York, thirty per cent. With the exceptions of some poor households, these wood fires in industrialized nations are lit mostly for aesthetic reasons: our love of the sight, smell and feel of wood heat. In upstate New York and Tennessee, I have joined the ranks of these burners, using a catalytic converter to reduce emissions, but now believe that, despite my love of their flames, inefficient wood-burning stoves can seldom be justified when we have access to alternatives. Living close to other people, the smoke from my wood stove harms neighbours more than it needs to or should. This is a sad conclusion. Wood heat taps our ancestral aesthetic love of controlled fire and, in some circumstances, can be less carbon intensive than other sources of heat. Yet, living in close proximity to others requires a new aesthetic, one less smoky and toxic.

The harm done by smoke from domestic burning of wood is now joined by the conflagration of forests, especially in areas close to significant human population centres. Although the overall area of burned land has decreased globally in the last two decades, mostly due to loss of savannah (which burns) to intensively managed cropland (which usually does not), forest fire is increasingly threatening the health of people and ecosystems. From Southeast Asia to the Amazon, from California to New South Wales, from Siberia to Africa, many of the world's forests are ablaze at a scale that rivals the fieriest times in Earth's prehistory.

My own initiation into how such fires affect human health came in 2020 when I lived close to the record-breaking forest fires in Colorado. Four fires over forty thousand hectares in size burned that year, along with many smaller ones, eclipsing all other years in extent. The heat and smoke from some reached twelve thousand metres high, creating huge pyrocumulonimbus clouds. The smoke and cloud were so dense that, standing on an adjacent mountain ridge on a bright afternoon, the entire northern half of the sky was covered in swirling grey and the land below looked dark as night. The sky looked that way for weeks, the intensity of the smoke and shadows depending on how strong the wind was each day. Our house, often downwind of plumes of smoke from fires that burned for months, was enveloped in a murk that ranged from the haziness of a smoky barroom to eerie dark orange, the only colour left after the dense smoke scattered and absorbed all other colours of daylight.

I became smoke. Clothes smelled of it. Fine ash found its way onto every household surface. The smoke wrapped itself into my senses and would not let go. A peppery sting in sinuses. An oily, metallic feel in the mouth. Every inhale felt insufficient, as if the acrid haze had displaced oxygen from the air. I could feel my lungs clenching. There was a sense of inescapability. Despite running an air filter inside the house continually for three months, the aroma, taste and bodily invasion of wood smoke assailed me.

The sensory burden of the smoke is exacerbated by the knowledge of what is burning and why. When a fire engulfs multiple square kilometres in one afternoon, then keeps moving and smouldering for weeks afterwards, few forest animals or plants can survive. In the hottest places, the burn leaves only mineral soil, a sandy, rocky remnant of a beautiful, diverse ecosystem. Elsewhere, every single tree is turned to a charred stump, with only silent white ash between. When I smelled the fire, I was inhaling the last bodily remains of plants and animals I had known and befriended on my walks in the mountains, turned now to clouds of gases and microscopic ash flecks. To inhale was to grieve.

The causes of ignition for these Colorado fires were diverse, from lightning, to sparks and cigarettes from vehicles, to arson. But the underlying cause was our collective behaviour. The mountain forests are drier and hotter than they have been for centuries. Warmth encourages prolific breeding of tree-killing beetles. Whole mountainsides are covered in mostly dead trees. In such conditions, fires that would, in past decades, have burned just a few hundred hectares, turn into blazes of magnitudes unknown in the recorded human history of the region. Yet, just east of the mountains, the frenzy of oil and gas drilling continues, amid an expanding sea of car-dependent suburbia. When the forest fires finally died out, in the first snows of winter, the haze changed to that caused by fossil fuel extraction and a culture addicted to our vehicles. We are the arsonists. To smell smoke is to understand our own complicity.

Globally, the smoke from the largest fires covers many countries. In 2015, forty million people in Southeast Asia swam for weeks in a pall of smoke from burning rainforests as thick as murky water. Direct economic losses were fifteen billion dollars.

Regardless of the region, the human body suffers in these fires. In the short term, during active burns, hospital visits for asthma, bronchitis, dyspnoea and chronic obstructive pulmonary disease all increase. In California, heart attacks and strokes surge during large burns. But the effects last much longer than the weeks or months when the fire is burning. Because smoke particles enter the body, prolonged inhalation of wood smoke ravages our heart and blood vessels, kills infants and stunts lungs. The 2015 Southeast Asian fires caused one hundred thousand premature deaths.

The forests that are now gone up in smoke, turned to gas and haze, were once our source of life: water, food, the ten thousand creatures, spirit, home and solace. We pyre what would have been our future. Dark smoke for our spirits and psyches.

Human ancestors thrived by learning to control fire. They found ways to partner with flames, opening new technological and social possibilities. We are all descendants of their canny skill. Even our genes bear fire's mark, adapting us to its presence. Now, we have lost control. Smoke teaches us that from the inside. In this new era that we have created, an era when smoke plumes from torched forests veil entire regions of the world, our genes, physiology and culture are so far unable to cope, unable to find wholesome life.

And so, what next?

Wood smoke has always called us into community, opening human possibility. For *Homo erectus*, our distant ancestors, fire kindled the first signs of human culture. For early *Homo sapiens*, fires were hubs both for technological progress and imaginative story-telling. Perhaps the modern crisis of forest burning also calls us into community and demands from us novel ideas and stories, but on a scale unknown to all previous peoples. It is no longer a campfire or hearth calling us, but the ancient forests themselves, as they blaze and die. Gather. Imagine. Act.

XII.

OLIVE OIL

Hills of the Eastern Mediterranean

VINTAGE: *circa* 6000 BCE

For most tree conversations, we humans are eavesdroppers. When we delight in the leafy, woodsy aroma of a forest or houseplant, we are responding not to chemical signals intended for us, but to the dozens of aromatic molecules that plants use to chat with one another and with insects and other animal species. Leaves converse about the weather and the state of the insects that are nibbling on them, using this information to coordinate growth and defences. Roots, too, signal to one another with aromatic molecules, directing their growing tips toward nutritive soil and away from stressful spots. The union of root and fungus is also mediated by chemicals, many of which are aromatic. The mushroomy, tangy, earthy smells of soil are the whispers that bind plants and fungi in the dark below-ground soil community. Flowers beckon to passing insects with odours evolved to be alluring to pollinators. The same is true of fruits whose colours, tastes, textures and aromas signal to animals: the sweet aroma of American pawpaw fruit, smelling like custard and pear, is irresistible to foxes and coyotes. European foxes and many rodents are likewise aficionados of the smell and taste of blackberries and wild strawberries. In tropical forests, birds, bats and primates all find and assess the fruits of figs and other species by nose. Plants actively manage their aromatic signalling to animals, switching on genes that produce smelly molecules as flowers open and fruits ripen.

The olive tree draws humans into this web of desires and chemical interconnections. In our sensual relationship with the olive, we are not eavesdroppers as we are with other plants. Instead, the olive intends its aromas for us. For eight millennia, olive trees and people have twinned their lives. Part of what binds us to them is their aroma.

I dip a piece of fresh baguette into a shallow dish of olive oil. A verdant smell rises, a mix of grasses and freshly cut artichoke. I am suffused with a sense of vigorous green, the smells of renewal during springtime. Alongside, I smell a hint of tart apple with peppery overtones. This is an aroma that promises an inner glow of satisfaction, a pleasing complement to bread and grain. The smell of olive oil activates my nose, my thoughts and my body's wordless needs, speaking directly to me. This is no accident. Evolution has carved knowledge of my senses into the olive tree's genome. Those trees that most effectively beguiled our senses were the ones we tended. We protected our favourites from fire, brought them water and cleared away competition. We replanted their seed, grafted twig cuttings and nurtured their sapling progeny. Human senses guided olive evolution. We did not just graft wood. Through agriculture and selective breeding, our noses and palates also grafted themselves into olive DNA.

Before Mediterranean humans joined their fate to that of the olive tree, birds were the dispersers of the trees' fruits. Song thrushes and blackcaps gobbled down the fruits, then winged the seeds away from the parent trees, depositing the digestion-resistant pips in convenient piles of fertilizer. Smaller birds like Sardinian warblers and European robins pecked at the flesh and occasionally managed to gulp down a seed. Bird beaks, drawn to the trees by hunger for oily flesh, were the olive trees' couriers. This is a common arrangement. Half of the tree and shrub species in the Mediterranean unite bird hunger and plant reproduction in this way. In tropical forests, ninety per cent of woody plants disperse their seeds via animal guts.

Human gullets are wider than those of birds and our taste for unctuous delight is keener. We prefer trees with especially large and oily fruits. Now, thanks to our selective breeding of trees, most olive fruits are too large for birds, although the song thrush still manages to swallow some whole. The flesh of these trees is plumper, each cell in the olive fruit's flesh swollen by an oil droplet within. After pressing, this oil yields a thrilling aroma to human noses, a promise of delight and satisfaction. We are powerfully motivated by unctuous fruity odours. Our nervous systems yearn for this aromatic promise of satiety, but birds seem to care little for olive's odorous signals. Those olives in orchards today are those that satisfied our hankering.

As with any parent entrusting its young to others, trees are picky about which species they summon. The shape, aroma and colour of fruits are tuned to the sensory particularity of the trees' favourite couriers. The form of fruit is a tree's answer to animal aesthetics. Red fruits attract the eyes of birds. Odours of decay summon mammalian scavengers. Primates are drawn in with fruity, sugary aromas. Migrating birds hunger for energy-rich oils and sugars. Humans are no exception. Any tree wishing to tie its fate to ours must beckon to our particular senses. When we dip our bread into a bowl of olive oil or pour some into a pan on the stovetop before tossing in vegetables, we enact an ancient sensory relationship.

During the last Ice Age, olives clung to life in small refugia around the Mediterranean. Genetic evidence suggests that these included the Strait of Gibraltar, parts of the Aegean Sea and the northeastern corner of the Mediterranean. Likely the climate was just warm enough in these spots to allow the trees to squeak through the chilly millennia. When the climate warmed, the trees, with the help of birds, spread from their hide-outs and colonized the lands all around the Mediterranean. It was not long before humans joined in. Starting about eight thousand years ago, on the border of what is now Syria and Turkey, and south in the areas that we now call Jordan, Israel and the West Bank, people started to eat olive's fruits and tend the trees. This practice spread all over the Mediterranean. The testimony of genes in trees today shows that this process involved both transport of favoured cultivars from one place to another and the domestication of local variants. In the western Mediterranean, for example, trees bear the genetic signature of African wild olives, a feature not present in trees to the east.

Over time, people deepened the sophistication of their labours on behalf of olive trees. We built irrigation canals and terraces, tilled and cleared the soil, groomed trees with pruning blades and mastered grafting and transplantation. The reward for those trees whose fruits appealed to human senses was the domination of fields and rocky hillsides all around the Mediterranean basin. The reward for humans, too, was abundance. Olives yield more nutrition from the seasonally arid land than any other crop. Leathery leaves retain moisture even in a hot, dry wind. Silvery hairs reflect excess sunlight. Roots ramify, burrow and find deep-buried water. By partnering with the olive tree, human civilizations in the region latched onto the productivity of a species with long experience of a climate where summers are often hot and rainless, but winters are moist and cool. Without olive trees, Knossos, Carthage, Jerusalem, Athens and Rome would have been modest villages. Mediterranean culture was, for millennia, founded on reciprocity with olive trees.

Olive oil reached northern parts of Europe, including the British Isles, intermittently over the last two millennia. Olive oil amphora were common in Roman Britain, indicating extensive trade with Southern Europe. Eighteenth-century records from the Port of London show imports of two-and-a-half thousand gallons of olive oil per week. Mrs Beeton's classic nineteenth-century British household management book discusses the use of olive oil for salads and recommends a 'tablespoonful of the best olive-oil on the top of each jar or bottle' of pickled onions, implying that British housekeepers not only used olive oil but made distinctions between 'best' and not-so-good olive oils. But in the mid-twentieth century olive oil was available in Britain only though speciality shops and its use was sometimes derided as an affectation of the upper middle classes, a curious situation for a food that, in Southern Europe, was a mainstay. Now, olive oil is in every British supermarket, a strange echo, perhaps, of Roman Britain.

Although they can thrive in arid conditions where many other agricultural plant species cannot, olives are more productive when summer's duress is eased by rains. Humans soon learned this and reshaped the flow of water across the land to benefit the trees. From contouring the land to direct water to trees, to building irrigation canals, to modern drip irrigation pipes and nozzles, human ingenuity has helped the trees to find water. Only decadal droughts or extended wars could break this life-giving bond between people and trees. When these calamities arrived, both human civilization and olive abundance crashed.

Other trees have yoked themselves to our noses and palates. Citrus, apples, coffee, tea, breadfruit, dates, hazel, Brazil nut, almond, oil palm, chestnut and dozens more. But none so completely as the olive (save perhaps the *Camellia sinensis* plants that give us tea, an entirely domesticated species). All around the Mediterranean, the boundaries between wild, feral and domestic olive trees are blurred, the result of eight millennia of melding between tree reproduction and horticulture. For human culture and the trees on which it depends, there is no boundary. Human society in the region is sustained by tree roots. Religion, art and culture remember this.

In all the Abrahamic religions, life and light are symbolized by olive branches or olive oil. The unending plenitude of olive oil is the ecological foundation of the miracle of the Jerusalem Temple, giving us the Jewish Festival of Lights. Jesus became the Christ, *khrīstós*, meaning the one anointed with olive oil. The light of Allah in the *Qur'an* is like that of a lamp fuelled with oil from a blessed olive tree 'whose oil almost gives light even when no fire touches it – light upon light'. When the Old Testament's destroying floodwaters ebbed, a dove wings to Noah, 'lo, in her mouth was an olive leaf pluckt off' – where olives grow, life is possible. For the ancient Greeks and Romans, too, olives were sacred trees, and olive branches and oil symbolized fruitfulness and plenitude. Athena gave Athens its greatest gift, the first olive tree, establishing her primacy among the gods there. Olympic champions were crowned in olive wreaths. The olive branch, then and now, signifies peace.

These images now also appear in lands where the olive did not grow, a cultural migration from the Mediterranean. Many bullion coins from the British Royal Mint show Britannia with an olive branch in her hand. An eagle on the American dollar bill clasps olive branches in talons and, on the other side, the numerals are wrapped by fruit-laden olive boughs. We modern humans might forget our dependence on the fruitfulness of the land, but our currency carries reminders of the rootedness of prosperity. Tellingly, no cryptocurrency symbols feature trees or vegetation of any kind, despite the prominent place of leaves and branches on many traditional banknotes and coins. Cryptocurrency is presently mostly 'mined' by intensive use of fossil fuels, without any reciprocity with living beings like trees.

The olive is not just a metaphor or symbol for peace, plenitude and the divine. In the Mediterranean and beyond, the olive tree is quite literally the origin and sustainer of life and goodness. Without the reciprocal relationship – the symbiosis – between people and olive trees, human life in the region would be far more meagre and restricted.

I bow my head to a bowl of olive oil and inhale the delicious aromas. I smell herbs, steeped in light butter. The aromatic sparkle of tomato leaves rubbed between fingers, too. Behind these welcoming sensations, a touch of bitter cypress.

In the heavenly odours of a bowl of olive oil, I understand the trees' message: the sacred does not descend upon us from on high. Peace and prosperity do not emerge from human hands alone. Goodness in life is an aroma rising from the living Earth, a result of the fruitful unions of humans and trees.

XIII.

BOOKS

Bookshelves worldwide

VINTAGE: *circa* 2500 BCE to present

Back at home after a shopping expedition, I slide a new book out of the bookshop's paper bag. I thumb open the book and plunge my nose between the pages, inhaling. A sweet rush: bright, tangy, with a faint undertone of wood. I fan the pages again and poke my nose deeper. Here, the odour is more intense, the warmth of fresh paper and ink combine with the acid bite of glue in the spine. Later, the words in this book will, I hope, bring me pleasure, but the first delight is aromatic. I save the pleasure for home. Sniffing books in a bookshop feels slightly deviant or gauche, a public exposure of a private pleasure. No matter, sometimes I'll sneak a sniff anyway, a clandestine huff of the spicy smell of the photos in a big art book, perhaps, or a whiff of chemically ink from the fat, thin-paged dictionary.

As a child, I greeted every book with a sniff. This habit gave me an informal hierarchy of book smells. At the bottom of my list were slick-paged textbooks made from coated paper. As a nerdy kid, I often enjoyed their words, but their pages smelled like the cross between an oil refinery and bleach. Likely these smells came from the synthetic chemicals – polyethylene, resin, or synthetic rubber, mixed with minerals – that gave the paper its sheen and the chlorine that bleached the paper white as porcelain. These vaguely toxic smells did not invite extended nasal investigation as I sat doing homework, but their industrial weirdness was fascinating nonetheless. Sneeze-inducing musty, mouldy books were likewise toward the bottom of the list, although the promise of a whiff from a truly rotten volume was perversely alluring. These damp unfortunates had yielded their aromatic personalities to the fungal kingdom. Next up the scale of bookish aromatic delight were new inexpensive paperbacks. These had a bright, uncomplicated aroma, a clean undertone of fresh paper, a mellow version of the smell of newly sawn dry pine wood, enlivened by the spice of ink. Higher still on the list were more expensive books, hardcovers or paperbacks printed on thicker, finger-pleasing papers. The smells of these was like those of cheaper paperbacks, but more complex, with darker tones: leather, coffee, smoke or even a hint of sulphurous egg or manure. Each hardcover had a different signature, and so opening these books promised surprise. At the top of my hierarchy of book aromas were very old books, especially those that had sat undisturbed in a warm, dry library. We had few of these at home, and so I looked forward to a sniff from a book on my grandparents' shelves. Later, when I went to university, I kept an eye out in the library for older volumes nestled between newer companions. I'd stop and pull out the elder, open its pages, then lower my head to inhale. Smoky vanilla. A hint of dark, rich soil. Sawdust, almonds and chocolate. These were calming sensations, as if the book were drawing me out of the tumult of the everyday, into deeper time and wider, restful perspective.

In adulthood, the hierarchy remains, although with some additions. I find old paperbacks unpredictable and therefore always interesting. Try poking your nose into a few. One of my favourite spots is under Waterloo Bridge, at the open-air Southbank Book Market, where tables are loaded with thousands of books, an emporium for readers and biblio-sniffers seeking aromatic diversity. The vanilla in some old paperbacks is as rich as any august tome in a grand library. But others, likely those made with low-lignin papers, are merely acerbic, like pine boards spritzed with vinegar. In contrast, the new paperbacks ranged in high-street bookshops smell less woody than they used to, a reflection of changes in pulping technologies that increased the efficiency of bleaching, digesting lignin and removing other undesirable molecules, while improving the printability and surface quality of the paper. In the classroom and office, the unpleasant odour of coated papers is less pronounced today, a result of the use of less aromatic thermoplastics as coatings. Gone, too, is the sweet scent of classroom handouts made with Banda or Ditto machines, each purple-inked sheet giving students a strong hit of the chlorofluorocarbons and alcohols used to carry the ink. Today, book printers also use mostly soya-based inks instead of those based on petroleum or rubber, an innovation from the 1980s that reduces toxic off-gassing.

My adulthood experience of book aromas is also changed by my tea- and coffee-drinking. As a child, I did not slurp caffeinated hot drinks through the day and so had little direct connection to their aromas. Now, I smell old books and am reminded of coffee shops and tea houses. This reminder is no coincidence. Coffee and darker teas (and chocolate) are produced partly by curing, fermenting or heating lignin and cellulose, and replicate some of the chemical processes in aging paper. The old book is, from the chemist's perspective, like a very, very well-steeped tea or a fine dark chocolate.

Maya Angelou writes of 'breathing in the world' during her childhood visits to the library. This marvellous and freeing breath came through stories. And so it is for all readers, our minds transported as we read words coming to us from other times and places, carried by ink and paper. We breathe in the world, too, through the aromas of ink and paper themselves, connecting to the physical and ecological roots of books.

Every library has its aromatic signature. The lobby and reading rooms of many are dominated by carpet fumes and the odour of ranks of public computers, a tingle of hot plastics and electronics, as befits institutions whose goal is now partly to make available the internet to all. I remember visiting City of London libraries as a child, and being comforted by the warmth of the carpet-computer-book aroma, a smell unique to libraries. Other libraries, especially the wood-panelled rooms of older universities, smell of wood polish and, in the front rooms, fresh newsprint. Back in the stacks, libraries are dominated by the warm aroma of books. No dust, no mould, just millions of well-tended sheets of paper slowly exhaling into their surroundings. The aromas are most delightful in the parts of the library that hold the oldest books. Here, pages hold words penned over a century ago. These venerable books warm the air with a mix of almond, vanilla and leather, with a faintly sweet, almost floral, overtone. An aroma of welcome and repose. In other parts of the library, smells range from sawdusty and sharp where paperback novels are kept, to a strange mix of fruit and engine oil in the sections housing older glossy periodicals.

The varied aromas of the library reveal that what we call 'paper' is a multifarious collection of substances. Older paper-making processes could not cleanse wood pulp of all its lignin, the molecule that gives wood its interior strength, nor did they reduce the acidity of paper pulp. Nineteenth-century paper therefore ages fast, rapidly becoming yellow and brittle. Older paper also releases a distinctive aroma, the product of its particular chemistry. As oxygen breaks lignin's interior chemical bonds, aromas are released to the air. The same is true for cellulose, the main molecule in wood and paper, which breaks down rapidly in the acidity of older papers. The aromas released from these old books include almondy furfural, sweet toluene, spiky formaldehyde and several molecules that smell like vanilla. Alongside these, dozens of other molecules add hints of earth, sweat or smoke. In contrast, the library stacks filled with more recent works are dominated either by the woody smells of acid-free paper, for the uncoated pages of paperbacks, or the pungency of synthetic glues, paper coatings and inks for coated papers.

Like the stories in their pages, book aromas are many-layered. No single molecule defines the smell of any book, old or young. All book nose-bouquets are mixtures, with many layers, inviting us into a complex sensory experience, if only we bow our heads to their pages and inhale. These aromas are indicators of the slow degradation of the books as paper turns to gas. Some of these gases can accelerate the process of deterioration. Acidic gases such as fumes of acetic acid or formaldehyde seep into other volumes, hastening the chemical breakdown of paper. A slight aroma of old books is harmless, but unventilated archives – so pleasantly redolent of ancient books to us – accelerate the aging of their charges.

It is not only libraries that bathe us in the aromas of old books. Antiquarian bookshops have the same richness as the archival sections of the library, often enhanced by the wooden and leather furnishings used by shop owners to create the right ambiance. Shops that deal in more recent second-hand books are more varied. In a few, the nose-tickle of dust and hints of mould suggest that some of the books may have arrived here from basements and attics, an ingathering of unwanted literature now ready to be disbursed to new homes. In others, we sniff the combined exhalations of thousands of paperbacks whose lower-quality papers are taking the first steps on the journey of disintegration: a mix of old pine planks and marzipan, with a touch of something earthy, like dry clay dust.

In Japan, the aroma of shops selling used books has received official recognition. The smells of the second-hand bookshops in Tokyo's Kanda district are on the Ministry of the Environment's *100 Good Fragrances of Japan* list, alongside seaweed shops, old-growth forests, plum blossoms, and the aromas of foods such as kimchi and eel. Perhaps we should follow the lead of the Japanese and list London's Southbank Book Market, the British Library and other significant book-aroma locales on a national registry?

The British candle-making supply company Craftovator and Powell's Books in Portland, Oregon, have tried to bottle the aromatic experience of books. The 'Vintage Bookstore Fragrance Oil' for candles delivers 'woody chypre…leather, bergamot pith, green leaves and warmer citrus notes'. Powell's promises in its 'unisex fragrance' to evoke 'a labyrinth of books; secret libraries; ancient scrolls; and cognac swilled by philosopher-kings', and perhaps also to keep the spirit of irony alive. A spritz onto my wrist from my bottle of their 'Eau de Bookstore' does have some of the leathery vanilla aromas of a bookshop, but then is overwhelmed by floral scents, like a bowl of flowery potpourri sitting atop a stack of used novels. This innovation suggests that every bookshop should sell a signature perfume, a reminder, however imperfect, of the delights of browsing the shelves. Judging by how fast Powell's perfume sold out when launched, these products could also give a useful boost to the bottom line, helping to keep bookshops in business. It is doubtful that 'Eau de Delivery Envelope' would do the same for anonymous online retailers.

What aromas will our reading habits now bequeath to future generations? Although acid-free, low-lignin papers will last much longer than their predecessors, likely many centuries without significant deterioration, their chemical stability means that they will lack the aromas of present-day old books. E-readers and tablets will last only a few decades, at most, and, apart from a few held in museums, will join the piles of electronic waste that our civilization leaves in its wake. Likely no one will pull a decrepit e-reader from a shelf just to inhale its venerable aroma. The components of these devices will degrade and yield only the sickly or bitter tangs of plasticizer, solder and circuit board.

Another, more dramatic and tragic future is possible: fire. In 1986, an arsonist lit a fire in the stacks of the Los Angeles Central Library. Four hundred thousand books were burned. It took over three hundred firefighters seven hours to extinguish the blaze. At its core, the paper-fuelled fire was so hot that flames burned clear. At the periphery, firefighters battled black, sooty smoke, the partly combusted remains of paper, book covers, shelving and furniture. Outside, on city pavements for blocks around, the air smelled of torched paper. Librarians who watched in anguish from outside told writer Susan Orlean that they remember the 'syrupy' odour of burning microfilm and the smell of 'heartbreak and ashes' as fragments of burned books floated down from the sky. The LA fire was the largest and most dramatic example of an unfortunately long history of library conflagrations. Julius Caesar burned ancient Alexandria and its library in an act of war. In 1981 Buddhist Sinhalese extremists burned the Jaffna Public Library, destroying over one hundred thousand books, including the only copies of many irreplaceable Hindu Tamil texts. Accidents have claimed libraries, too. One of the historically most significant collections of British books and manuscripts – Magna Carta, Lindisfarne Gospels, Beowulf, royal papers and more – was badly damaged when a fireplace fire got out of control and burned the library of Sir Robert Cotton in 1731. The charred remnants formed one of the foundational collections at the British Museum. One hundred thousand volumes were lost after an electrical fault started a fire at Norwich Central Library in 1994. In 2014, a fire at the Mackintosh Library at Glasgow School of Art torched not only books, but the old-growth longleaf pine and tulipwood that had been used to build its interior, the most well-known building of famed architect Charles Rennie Mackintosh. The smoke of burning books and timbers is, unfortunately, part of the smell of libraries.

Other book burnings are manifestations of hate directed at particular peoples or ideas: antisemites have burned Jewish texts for centuries in Europe and the Nazis turned this practice into state policy. Constantine ordered heretical books burned, as have religious and political fanatics across the ages. Ever since humans learned to write on papyrus and paper, books and scrolls have burned. The violence of this erasure has taken many forms, all of which transform human thought into ash.

Authors, too, use fire's literal and symbolic power to silence, applying the flame to their own work. From Franz Kafka to Gerard Manley Hopkins to Emily Dickinson, smoke has transformed words into vapours. When I lived in a house with a wood stove for heat, I found the finality of the act of burning early drafts of my books satisfying. The quick, bright flames and acrid smoke raised pages full of hopelessly tangled words into brief, nose-tingling life, before erasing them.

The aroma of burned paper, then, is a reminder of the ephemerality of language. Until we invented writing, all words lived in air, on the breath. Paper smoke is a return to origins, sometimes by choice, often as an act of oppression.

The aromas of books – whether a new paper-back, an ancient tome or a burned manuscript – tell us of the materiality, the sensuality of writing and reading. In writing down and sharing our thoughts, we enlist the help of substances beyond the human to help connect us one to another. At first, these were clay tablets or pieces of etched bone. Then, papyrus, mulberry and rag. Now, it is mostly trees that give us books. In this afterlife, trees continue the work of their lives as breathing, conversing organisms, uniting communities into communicative networks. In forests, trees are life-giving hubs for conversation among woodland creatures, knitting plant, fungus, animal and microbe. In books, pulped and processed trees do the same for humans, uniting us into the diverse and fruitful webs that we call culture. The aroma of books reminds us that this culture is possible only because of our relationships with the non-human.

Crack open a book. Sniff: literature is built on connections with trees, paper factories and ink pigments. *We breathe in the world.*

THE AROMAS OF TREES:

SIX PRACTICES

Aroma is the primary language of trees. They talk with molecules, conspiring with one another, beckoning fungi, scolding insects and whispering to microbes. Aroma is also our primal tongue, a direct link to memory and emotion, an inheritance from the communicative networks that sustained the first animal cells. The tens of millions of receptors in our nasal passages are ready to listen, able to discern minute differences among mixtures of aromatic molecules. The English language is too meagre to categorize this multiplicity, but bodies know how to respond. Our noses, though, need our help. Conscious intention

– the choice to slow down, inhale and consider a smell – allows sensory awareness to activate and blossom.

As a child, my nose poked everywhere. Between the pages of a freshly printed newspaper, into the spice jars of the kitchen, over the goods at the fish market and cheesemonger's, through steam from pots on the stove and among the leaves of the garden. Later, grown older, I forgot to attend in this way. My eyes and ears asserted their self-proclaimed supremacy. And so it is for much of our culture. Architecture aims to please the eye. Music, the ear. The internet reinforces this pre-existing bias, imperiously eliminating all senses except the visual and aural. To stop and smell is to reclaim a part of our humanity, to get back into our bodies and connect with the living creatures around us. It is also fun.

The rich, layered aroma of a ponderosa pine growing in the mountains of Colorado called me back to the practices of my childhood. Sitting under its boughs, I reawakened to the delights of odour, especially the diverse smells of trees, and the playful curiosity that comes from following my nose. Paying attention to the ponderosa pine's many-layered odours, I felt that some of the tree had flowed into me, lodging its stories in my body. Since then, tree aromas have been my teachers and my guides.

Every tree offers us a wordless sensory experience, a connection that unites human bodies and consciousness to the inner worlds of plants. This encounter is reward enough. But the particular aroma of a tree also contains stories, past and present. Our human aesthetic experience is a doorway to the trees' histories, ecologies and connections to human culture.

As you smell trees, try both a deep in-drawing of breath through the nostrils, then, after a rest, short, sharp sniffs. These two methods change the rate at which aromatic molecules hit your sensory cells: a slow caress and a vigorous rush. The combination opens aromatic layers of experience. The following invitations are suggested approaches to becoming more attuned to tree aromas, to becoming a sylvan sommelier. I invite you also to find and share your own.

Invitation I: At Home

Treat your nose to an inventory of the trees in your home. Lift a cup of tea to your nose. Camellia leaves, redolent of East Asian mountains. Wild *Camellia sinensi*s was domesticated independently at least three times – twice in China and once in India – starting over four thousand years ago. The aromas in my cuppa have old roots, a legacy of millennia of selective breeding. Domesticated coffee has a younger pedigree, dating back fifteen hundred years, originally from the highlands of southwestern Ethiopia, the Boma Plateau of Sudan and Mount Marsabit in Kenya. Dig your thumb into orange peel. Sharp oils, deterrents for hungry insects; originally from the Himalayan foothills. Unscrew the cinnamon jar. Whose hands peeled this bark from the coppiced tree? What other tree aromas live in your house? Dates and olives. Pencil shavings. Almond milk. Furniture wood, its odour gagged by varnish. Honey, laden with aromatic memories of tree nectar and pollen. Gin. Maple syrup. Inhale, and remember that we live in the forest, even when this truth is hidden from the eye.

Invitation II: Walking the Neighbourhood

Seek out the aromatic expressions of trees around your home. Let your hands help. Roll leaves and needles between fingertips. What is the character and disposition of each species? Spiky or lush? Reminiscent of grass, or seaweed, or spice? Rest your hands on bark, feel its texture, then draw your face close. Gently rub. What aromas linger in the crevices of the tree's surface? Does the tree proclaim its inner drama to the world or does it hold its personality close, revealing odour only through pruning cuts or insect holes? When the wind blows, do you smell any hint of tree? Upwind trees loose their aromas to the sky, seeding clouds and perfuming air. Turn to the wind and seek the trees' breath. During rain, remember that every raindrop was born by coalescing around a speck, often a clump of aromatic molecules from a tree. When the rain falls, head to a park, forest or street tree. Inhale and gulp down the aromas awakened and lifted up by raindrops.

Invitation III: At Your Bookshelf

First, consider your book-sniffing technique. The trick is to keep the aromas undisturbed until you are ready to huff them into your nostrils. Pulling from the top of the book's spine, gently tip the volume back from the shelf, making sure that the book's pages stay closed. Then, crack open the pages and plunge in your nose, drawing in the delicious page aromas as you do. Or, if this diver's method seems too brusque, try holding your nose close, then fanning the pages. The riffling motion of sheets against air stirs a breeze of aromas. Like a dog getting a blast of delight as it hangs out of a car window, our nasal passages get a rush of sensation. Dip into several books. What blends of ink and fibre do you detect in each? What do these sensations suggest about the provenance and age of each? Pick out a motley assemblage of volumes, including whatever magazines and letters you have lying around, and group them by aroma. Which is your favourite? What would you advise publishers as they consider the aromatic signatures of their works?

Invitation IV: Aromas Across Time and Space

We use trees to locate ourselves. What time of year is it? The leaves, sap and buds give us the answer. Where are we? The species that grow outside tell us: a maple tree visible on a hillside, yew in the churchyard, purple-flowered jacaranda in the park, hawthorn and hazel in the hedges, sapling plane tree on the street or thick-girthed oak behind the houses. Every tree species has its habitat and place, sometimes expanded by the work of horticulturalists. Invite your nose into this place-seeking. As you move through seasons and across the land, connect your blood to the trees' messages. Pause, get close and suck in the odours. Sketch a calendar of the tree-aroma seasons. What tree odours are most characteristic of each month? As you travel, keep a diary of what the trees reveal. Does springtime sap awaken before leaves? Do mountain trees have a different signature than their lowland cousins? In the late summer drought that threatens the survival of the trees on your street, what do you smell in their leaves and bark? How might you help them?

Is the aroma of springtime rainfall in the park different from that evoked by autumn showers? There are aromatic rhythms and maps awaiting us, tree languages of the land.

Invitation V: Your Roots

The roots of trees and human culture are entwined. Trees centre our stories of origin, meaning and life. Yggdrasil, the ash that connects the nine worlds of the Norse. The olives of the Abrahamic religions. The Buddha's *bodhi* fig tree. Plum and cherry blossoms in spring. Winter solstice fir boughs. The giant ceiba trees of tropical forests. Trees inhabit these stories not only as metaphors, but as reminders that human life exists always in relation to other beings. Sensual connection to trees teaches us this lesson from the inside out. What trees dwell in the stories of your family and culture? Find the tales, then seek out the physical experience of these trees. Bring their stories back into lived experience. Hold, inhale, gaze and hear them. Savour your roots, then excavate meaning. What convergences of sensory ecology and culture are celebrated in your stories and rituals? What new rituals might we graft onto these older practices, celebrations of connection suited for today?

Invitation VI: Tell Others

What tree aromas from the forest, city street or kitchen can we offer to our children and friends? The stories we tell alongside these sensual experiences knit memories that serve as guides. No other sense burrows as fast and deep into our understanding of meaning and emotion. By creating moments where tree aromas and human emotions converge, we craft strong memories and knit the human and beyond-human worlds. On a mountain slope, a teacher invites students to smell the loamy soil and piney tree bark, and grasp that the lives of soil and trees are one. In the city, the contrast between the aromas of the park and those of the untreed street convey a lesson about the vitality of the air, plants and human lungs. At the stove, a child learns that the pleasures of food emerge from the joy of connection between plants and people. Cuisine is an art that draws ecology and culture into satisfying, life-giving relationship. On a busy street corner, we smell the ephemeral flowers of city trees and understand that the forest enfolds us everywhere.

What stories will you share as you invite friends and family to inhale the trees?

By inviting others into these sensory pleasures, we not only share pleasure and curiosity in the moment, we also give the future a valuable gift: the memory of how trees and humans are bound together. In a world of tumultuous change and crisis, these sensory impressions of today are the raw material of collective memory. The generations that come after us will have no living memory of our time. They will need our stories. By paying attention, we will have true stories to give, stories grounded in lived, sensual relationship, unmediated by algorithms and intermediaries.

Inhale. Enjoy the aroma. Puzzle over it. Share the story.

THE MUSIC
OF TREES

David Haskell's aroma essays were conceived long before Covid, but now, to me, they are a rich reminder of what is waiting for us out there, beyond the four walls that have held us in isolation for so long. Our flat rectangles of digital freedom brought us amazing content, and we learned marvellous new ways to connect, but our bodies yearn for more. Just as no Zoom can bring us the warm fuzziness of a grandchild's cheek on our lips or the full resonance of a friend's laugh, there is no digital substitute for the sensory experience waiting out there in a forest or along a city pavement.

I was delighted, and more than a little intimidated, when David asked if I would write short compositions to accompany his aroma essays. While I have spent a lifetime playing music, writing it has always been daunting. But the idea of translating aromas into tones, rhythms and sonic textures was compelling. I have been keenly aware of sensory experience all my life, not with David's laser-sharp perception or careful attention, but more in the way of a mad scientist (admittedly heavier in alchemy than science), absorbing, mixing, layering, recombining all manner of input in my mind. My experience is of synthesis, where sounds come to me as colours, aromas almost as tactile sensations.

During the pandemic I missed my body's messy, jumbled up way of taking it all in, great gobs of sensation competing for attention, eventually settling into semi-sensible patterns that are my way to embrace the world. These short pieces gave me a space to have some fun with sensory material. My own experiences of these trees, alongside David's fantastically evocative words, created a road map of cross-sensory connection, and to my surprise these works mostly came quickly.

I have spent thousands of hours of my life holding maple and spruce, ebony and rosewood against my body in the form of a violin. The scents of varnish and rosin have been constants. The resonance of wood under my ear has given me my livelihood and my sense of self. These trees, harvested decades or centuries ago, will continue to grace the world with sound long after I am gone, a thought that always makes me smile. Trees are important to me.

The scents surrounding the trees in these essays are complex, from those the trees produce themselves to the human-created scents that compete and coalesce with them. I have used a variety of techniques to reflect that diversity – col legno (using the wood of the bow, rather than the hair), rubbing rosin onto bow hair, scordatura tuning (tuning strings to unusual pitches), pizzicato (plucking) and ponticello (playing with the bow against the violin's bridge). There are hints of real tunes (as any aficionado of summertime-street treats will detect in basswood) and new tunes meant to sound old (what does the age of an Australian beech sound like?). Consonance and dissonance are comfort and discomfort, although not necessarily always ordered that way. Aromas are full of colourful auditory possibility. My hope is to offer listeners one way to hear the smell of a tree, with the door left open for infinite other possibilities.

Katherine Lehman

You can hear the violin compositions that accompany the thirteen essays in this book through the links at soundcloud.com/katherinelehman/albums and in the audiobook edition.

Acknowledgements

This book grew from an essay in *Emergence Magazine*, a work that originated in conversations with Emmanuel Vaughan-Lee. I thank Emmanuel for the many ways that our work together has catalysed these and other ideas. I thank *Emergence Magazine* for permission to expand the original essay into this book.

I am grateful to Katherine Lehman for being my enthusiastic and creative companion during these explorations of tree aromas. My parents, Jean and George Haskell, provided excellent leads for many of the stories in this book and remembered more clearly than I what a nose-poker I was as a child. Suzanne Dalton helped me to clarify my memories of conker-picking at her house many years ago and Donald Dalton built the toy train that I reference here. Conversations with Joseph Bordley and Marianne Tyndall gave me new insights into tree aromas.

Stephanie Jackson, Kate Adams and their colleagues at Octopus Publishing Group are a delight to work with and have an inspiring vision for bringing works about the beyond-human world to readers. My agent Alice Martell, The Martell Agency, is a wonderful advocate and guide. I thank Stephanie Finman at The Martell Agency for invaluable help, and Caspian Dennis and Sandy Violette at Abner Stein for their excellent work.

Thank you, reader, for joining me in this exploration of tree aromas. May your nose lead you to delight, curiosity and wonder, with the help of our cousins, the trees.

Bibliography

Abel, E L, 'The gin epidemic: much ado about what?' in *Alcohol and Alcoholism* (2001), 36(5), 401–405

Achan, J, Talisuna, A O, Erhart, A, Yeka, A, Tibenderana, J K, Baliraine, F N, Rosenthal, P J & D'Alessandro, U, 'Quinine, an old anti-malarial drug in a modern world: role in the treatment of malaria' in *Malaria Journal* (2011), 10(1), 1–12

Alejo-Armijo, A, Altarejos, J & Salido, S, 'Phytochemicals and biological activities of laurel tree (*Laurus nobilis*)' in *Natural Product Communications* (2017), 12(5), 1934578X1701200519

Andela, N, Morton, D C, Giglio, L, Chen, Y, van der Werf, G R, Kasibhatla, P S, DeFries, R S, Collatz, G J, Hantson, S, Kloster, S, Bachelet, D, Forrest, M, Lasslop, G, Li, F, Mangeon, S, Melton, J R, Yue, C & Randerson, J T, 'A human-driven decline in global burned area' in *Science* (2017), 356(6345), 1356–1362

Atkinson, N, 'Ash dieback: one of the worst tree disease epidemics could kill 95% of UK's ash trees, in *The Conversation* (2019), https://theconversation.com/ash-dieback-one-of-the-worst-tree-disease-epidemics-could-kill-95-of-uks-ash-trees-116567

Beaumont, P B, 'The edge: More on fire-making by about 1.7 million years ago at Wonderwerk Cave in South Africa' in *Current Anthropology* (2011), 52(4), 585–595

Bembibre, C, & Strlič, M, 'Smell of heritage: a framework

for the identification, analysis and archival of historic odours' in *Heritage Science* (2017), 1–11

Berna, F, Goldberg, P, Horwitz, L K, Brink, J, Holt, S, Bamford, M & Chazan, M, 'Microstratigraphic evidence of in situ fire in the Acheulean strata of Wonderwerk Cave, Northern Cape province, South Africa' in *Proceedings of the National Academy of Sciences* (2012), 109(20), E1215–E1220

Besnard, G, Khadari, B, Navascués, M, Fernández-Mazuecos, M, El Bakkali, A, Arrigo, N, Baali-Cherif, D, Bronzini de Caraffa, V, Santoni, S, Vargas, P & Savolainen, V, 'The complex history of the olive tree: from Late Quaternary diversification of Mediterranean lineages to primary domestication in the northern Levant' in *Proceedings of the Royal Society B: Biological Sciences* (2013), 280(1756), 20122833

Beeton, I, *The Book of Household Management*, (1861), www.gutenberg.org/cache/epub/10136/pg10136.html

Besnard, G, Terral, J F & Cornille, A, 'On the origins and domestication of the olive: a review and perspectives' in *Annals of Botany* (2018), 121(3), 385–403

Black, C, Tesfaigzi, Y, Bassein, J A & Miller, L A, 'Wildfire smoke exposure and human health: significant gaps in research for a growing public health issue' in *Environmental Toxicology and Pharmacology* (2017), 55, 186–195

Blomquist, G J, Figueroa-Teran, R, Aw, M, Song, M, Gorzalski, A, Abbott, N L...& Tittiger, C, 'Pheromone production in bark beetles' in *Insect Biochemistry and Molecular Biology* (2010), 40(10), 699–712

Brittingham, A, Hren, M T, Hartman, G, Wilkinson,

K N, Mallol, C, Gasparyan, B & Adler, D S, 'Geochemical evidence for the control of fire by Middle Palaeolithic hominins' in *Scientific Reports* (2019), 9(1), 1–7

Bundjalung-Yugambeh Dictionary. 'Beech/Waygargah' https://bundjalung.dalang.com.au/language/view_word/4623

Bundjalung-Yugambeh Dictionary. 'The Bundjalung Dictionary' https://bundjalung.dalang.com.au/plugin_wiki/page/dictionary

Bushdid, C, Magnasco, M O, Vosshall, L B & Keller, A, 'Humans can discriminate more than 1 trillion olfactory stimuli' in *Science* (2014), 343(6177), 1370–1372

Cárdenas-Rodríguez, N, González-Trujano, M E, Aguirre-Hernández, E, Ruíz-García, M, Sampieri, A, Coballase-Urrutia, E & Carmona-Aparicio, L, 'Anticonvulsant and antioxidant effects of *Tilia americana* var. *mexicana* and flavonoids constituents in the pentylenetetrazole-induced seizures' in *Oxidative Medicine and Cellular Longevity* (2014), 2014, 329172

Chiu, C C, Keeling, C I & Bohlmann, J, 'Toxicity of pine monoterpenes to mountain pine beetle' in *Scientific Reports* (2017), 7(1), 1–8

Cincinelli, A, Martellini, T, Amore, A, Dei, L, Marrazza, G, Carretti, E, Belosi, F, Ravegnani, F & Leva, P, 'Measurement of volatile organic compounds (VOCs) in libraries and archives in Florence (Italy)' in *Science of the Total Environment* (2016), 572, 333–339

Coffey, G, 'Beer Street: Gin Lane. Some views of

18th-century drinking' in *Quarterly Journal of Studies on Alcohol* (1966), 27(4), 669–692

Constabel, C P, Yoshida, K & Walker, V, 'Diverse ecological roles of plant tannins: plant defense and beyond' in *Recent Advances in Polyphenol Research* (2014), 4, 115–142

Craftovator. Vintage Bookstore Fragrance, https://www.craftovator.co.uk/candle-making/vintage-bookstore-fragrance-oil/

Crane, P R, *Ginkgo: the Tree that Time Forgot* (2013), Yale University Press: New Haven

Croft, D P, Cameron, S J, Morrell, C N, Lowenstein, C J, Ling, F, Zareba, W, Hopke, P K, Utell, M J, Thurston, S W, Chalupa, D, Thevenet-Morrison, K, Evans, K A & Rich, D Q, 'Associations between ambient wood smoke and other particulate pollutants and biomarkers of systemic inflammation, coagulation and thrombosis in cardiac patients' in *Environmental Research* (2017), 154, 352–361

Del Tredici, P, 'Wake up and smell the ginkgos' in *Arnoldia* (2008), 66, 11–21

Fenech, A, Strlič, M, Cigić, I K, Levart, A, Gibson, L T, de Bruin, G, Ntanos, K, Kolar, J & Cassar, M, 'Volatile aldehydes in libraries and archives' in *Atmospheric Environment* (2010), 44(17), 2067–2073

Fitzky, A C, Sandén, H, Karl, T, Fares, S, Calfapietra, C, Grote, R, Saunier, A & Rewald, B, 'The interplay between ozone and urban vegetation – BVOC emissions, ozone deposition, and tree ecophysiology' in *Frontiers in Forests and Global Change* (2019), 2, 50

Goss, A, 'Building the world's supply of quinine: Dutch colonialism and the origins of a global pharmaceutical industry' in *Endeavour* (2014), 38(1), 8–18

Haack, R A, Jendak, E, Houping, L, Marchant, K R, Petrice, T R, Poland, T M & Ye, H, 'The emerald ash borer: a new exotic pest in North America' in *Newsletter of the Michigan Entomological Society* (2002), 47, 1–5

Hansell, A, Ghosh, R E, Blangiardo, M, Perkins, C, Vienneau, D, Goffe, K, Briggs, D & Gulliver, J, 'Historic air pollution exposure and long-term mortality risks in England and Wales: prospective longitudinal cohort study' in *Thorax* (2016), 71(4), 330-338

Hubbard, T D, Murray, I A, Bisson, W H, Sullivan, A P, Sebastian, A, Perry, G H, Jablonski, N G & Perdew, G H, 'Divergent Ah receptor ligand selectivity during hominin evolution' in *Molecular Biology and Evolution* (2016), 33(10), 2648–2658

Hussain, A, Rodriguez-Ramos, J C & Erbilgin, N, 'Spatial characteristics of volatile communication in lodgepole pine trees: evidence of kin recognition and intra-species support' in *Science of the Total Environment* (2019), 692, 127–135

Kikut-Ligaj, D & Trzcielińska-Lorych, J, 'How taste works: cells, receptors and gustatory perception' in *Cellular and Molecular Biology Letters* (2015), 20(5), 699–716

Kiyomizu, T, Yamagishi, S, Kume, A & Hanba, Y T, 'Contrasting photosynthetic responses to ambient air pollution between the urban shrub *Rhododendron × pulchrum* and urban tall tree *Ginkgo biloba* in Kyoto city: stomatal and leaf mesophyll morpho-anatomies are key traits' in *Trees* (2019), 33(1), 63–77

Lamorena, R B & Lee, W, 'Influence of ozone concentration and temperature on ultra-fine particle and gaseous volatile organic compound formations generated during the ozone-initiated reactions with emitted terpenes from a car air freshener' in *Journal of Hazardous Materials* (2008), 158(2–3), 471–477

Lamy, E, Pinheiro, C, Rodrigues, L, Capela-Silva, F, Lopes, O, Tavares, S & Gaspar, R, 'Determinants of tannin-rich food and beverage consumption: oral perception vs. psychosocial aspects' in *Tannins: Biochemistry, Food Sources and Nutritional Properties* (2016), (29–58). Nova Science Publishers: Hauppage

LittleTrees.com, 'About us', www.littletrees.com/about

Medieval manuscripts blog, 'Fire, Fire! The Tragic Burning of the Cotton Library', 23 October 2016, https://blogs.bl.uk/digitisedmanuscripts/2016/10/fire-fire-the-tragic-burning-of-the-cotton-library.html

Naeher, L P, Brauer, M, Lipsett, M, Zelikoff, J T, Simpson, C D, Koenig, J Q & Smith, K R, 'Woodsmoke health effects: a review' in *Inhalation Toxicology* (2007), 19(1), 67–106

Nevo, O, Razafimandimby, D, Jeffrey, J A J, Schulz, S & Ayasse, M, 'Fruit scent as an evolved signal to primate seed dispersal' in *Science Advances* (2018), 4(10), eaat4871

Orlean, S, *The Library Book* (2019), Simon & Schuster: New York

Parliment, T H, 'Characterization of the putrid aroma compounds of *Ginkgo biloba* fruits', AGRIS (1995)

Pearce, F, 'People today are still dying early from high

1970s air pollution' in *New Scientist* (2016), https://www.newscientist.com/article/2076728-people-today-are-still-dying-early-from-high-1970s-air-pollution/

Philip, K, 'Imperial science rescues a tree: global botanic networks, local knowledge and the transcontinental transplantation of *Cinchona*' in *Environment and History* (1995), 1(2), 173–200

Puech, J L, Feuillat, F & Mosedale, J R, 'The tannins of oak heartwood: structure, properties, and their influence on wine flavor' in *American Journal of Enology and Viticulture* (1999), 50(4), 469–478

Rees-Owen, R L, Gill, F L, Newton, R J, Ivanović, R F, Francis, J E, Riding, J B.... & dos Santos, R A L, 'The last forests on Antarctica: reconstructing flora and temperature from the Neogene Sirius Group, Transantarctic Mountains' in *Organic Geochemistry* (2018), 118, 4–14

Rodríguez, A, Alquézar, B & Peña, L, 'Fruit aromas in mature fleshy fruits as signals of readiness for predation and seed dispersal' in *New Phytologist* (2013), 197, 36–48

Rodríguez-Sánchez, F & Arroyo, J, 'Reconstructing the demise of Tethyan plants: climate-driven range dynamics of *Laurus* since the Pliocene' in *Global Ecology and Biogeography* (2008), 17(6), 685–695

Sämann, J, US Patent No. 2,757,957A (1956), Washington, DC: US Patent and Trademark Office

Sämann, J, US Patent No. 3,065,915A (1962), Washington, DC: US Patent and Trademark Office

Schraufnagel, D E, Balmes, J R, Cowl, C T, De Matteis, S, Jung, S H, Mortimer, K...& Wuebbles,

D J, 'Air pollution and noncommunicable diseases: a review by the Forum of International Respiratory Societies' Environmental Committee, Part 2: Air pollution and organ systems' in *Chest* (2019), 155(2), 417–426

Seybold, S J, Huber, D P, Lee, J C, Graves, A D & Bohlmann, J, 'Pine monoterpenes and pine bark beetles: a marriage of convenience for defense and chemical communication' in *Phytochemistry Reviews* (2006), 5(1), 143–178

Sheil, D, 'Forests, atmospheric water and an uncertain future: the new biology of the global water cycle' in *Forest Ecosystems* (2018), 5(1), 1–22

Shimada, T, 'Salivary proteins as a defense against dietary tannins' in *Journal of Chemical Ecology* (2006), 32(6), 1149–1163

Smallwood, P D, Steele, M A & Faeth, S H, 'The ultimate basis of the caching preferences of rodents, and the oak-dispersal syndrome: tannins, insects, and seed germination' in *American Zoologist* (2001), 41(4), 840–851

Smith, R, 'Xylem monoterpenes of pines: distribution, variation, genetics, function' in *Gen. Tech. Rep. PSW-GTR-177* (2000), Albany, CA: Pacific Southwest Research Station, United States Forest Service

Strlič, M, Thomas, J, Trafela, T, Cséfalvayová, L, Kralj Cigić, I, Kolar, J & Cassar, M, 'Material degradomics: on the smell of old books' in *Analytical Chemistry* (2009), 81(20), 8617–8622

Taban, A, Saharkhiz, M J & Niakousari, M, 'Sweet bay (*Laurus nobilis L.*) essential oil and its chemical composition, antioxidant activity and leaf micro-morphology under different extraction methods' in *Sustainable Chemistry and Pharmacy* (2018), 9, 12–18

Thomas, P A, Alhamd, O, Iszkuło, G, Dering, M & Mukassabi, T A, 'Biological flora of the British Isles: *Aesculus hippocastanum*' in *Journal of Ecology* (2019), 107(2), 992–1030

Times (London), 'Goods imported into the Port of London from Tuesday Jan 24th, to Tuesday the 31st of Jan', Issue 349, 6 February 1786

Trimmer, C, Keller, A, Murphy, N R, Snyder, L L, Willer, J R, Nagai, M H , Katsanis, N, Vosshall, L B, Matsunami, H & Mainland, J D, 'Genetic variation across the human olfactory receptor repertoire alters odor perception' in *Proceedings of the National Academy of Sciences* (2019), 116(19), 9475–9480

United Kingdom Department for Environment, Food and Rural Affairs, 'National Statistics: emissions of air pollutants in the UK – summary', www.gov.uk/ government/statistics/emissions-of-air-pollutants/ emissions-of-air-pollutants-in-the-uk-summary

Vohra, K, Vodonos, A, Schwartz, J, Marais, E A, Sulprizio, M P & Mickley, L J, 'Global mortality from outdoor fine particle pollution generated by fossil fuel combustion: results from GEOS-Chem' in *Environmental Research* (2021), 195, 110754

Vu, T P, Kim, S H, Lee, S B, Shim, S G, Bae, G N & Sohn, J R, 'Nanoparticle formation from a commercial air freshener at real-exposure concentrations of ozone' in *Asian Journal of Atmospheric Environment* (2011), 5(1), 21–28

Walker, K, & Nesbit, M, 'Just the tonic: a natural

history of tonic water', Kew Publishing online (19 October 2019), www.kew.org/read-and-watch/just-the-tonic-history

Waring, M S, Wells, J R & Siegel, J A, 'Secondary organic aerosol formation from ozone reactions with single terpenoids and terpenoid mixtures' in *Atmospheric Environment* (2011), 45(25), 4235–4242

Wettstein, Z S, Hoshiko, S, Fahimi, J, Harrison, R J, Cascio, W E & Rappold, A G, 'Cardiovascular and cerebrovascular emergency department visits associated with wildfire smoke exposure in California in 2015' in *Journal of the American Heart Association* (2018), 7(8), e007492

Wollenweber, E, Stevens, J F, Dörr, M & Rozefelds, A C, 'Taxonomic significance of flavonoid variation in temperate species of *Nothofagus*' in *Phytochemistry* (2003), 62(7), 1125–1131

World Health Organization, 'Household air pollution and health', 8 May 2018, https://www.who.int/news-room/fact-sheets/detail/household-air-pollution-and-health

Wrangham, R, 'Control of fire in the Paleolithic: evaluating the cooking hypothesis' in *Current Anthropology* (2017), 58(S16), S303–S313

Wu, G A, Terol, J, Ibanez, V et al, 'Genomics of the origin and evolution of *Citrus*' in *Nature* (2018), 554(7692), 311–316

About the Composer

Katherine Lehman is a violinist, arts leader and educator creating a new vision for music as a pathway to justice and connection. From humans to old-growth forest trees, opening our ears to unheard stories enriches us all. As Executive Director of the Boulder Philharmonic, she was nationally recognized for asking musicians to listen first, creating music to amplify and empower communities. She has received awards from the National Endowment for the Arts, ASCAP, and the League of American Orchestras. She served on the faculty at the University of the South in Sewanee, TN, and was Director of the Sewanee Summer Music Festival. A prolific performer and recording artist, she her discography includes albums, films, and videogames. Lehman studied at the Eastman School of Music and Northwestern University.

About the Author

David Haskell is a writer and biologist known for his rich integration of science, poetry and attention to the living world. His two previous books, *The Forest Unseen* and *The Songs of Trees*, won numerous awards, including the US National Academies' Best Book Award, finalist for the Pulitzer Prize in non-fiction, Reed Environmental Writing Award, National Outdoor Book Award, Iris Book Award and John Burroughs Medal. Born in London and brought up in France, he has lived for the last thirty years in various parts of the United States, including Tennessee, Colorado and New York, finding new aromatic delights in the trees of each place. Haskell received his BA from the University of Oxford and PhD from Cornell University. He is a Guggenheim Fellow and Professor at the University of the South in Sewanee, Tennessee. Find him at dghaskell.com or on social media: 🐦 @DGHaskell, 📷 🗗 DavidGeorgeHaskell